Papers presented at


**SLUDGE DIGESTER MIXING AND HEATING SYSTEMS**
**Cranfield, UK: 22 May 2001**
*and*
**SLUDGE MANAGEMENT**
**Cranfield, UK: 23 May 2001**

**Published by**
**BHR Group Limited**
**The Fluid Engineering Centre**
**Cranfield**
**Bedfordshire MK43 0AJ**
**United Kingdom**
**Tel: +44 1234 750422**
**Fax: +44 1234 750074**

**SLUDGE DIGESTER MIXING AND HEATING SYSTEMS**
Cranfield, UK: 22 May 2001
*and*
**SLUDGE MANAGEMENT**
Cranfield, UK: 23 May 2001

# EDITORIAL NOTES

This volume contains material presented at the above events held at Cranfield University on 22 and 23 May 2001.

The views expressed in the papers are those of the authors and do not necessarily represent the views of BHR Group Limited.

BHR Group Limited
The Fluid Engineering Centre
Cranfield
Bedfordshire MK43 0AJ
United Kingdom
Tel:   01234 750422
Fax:   01234 750074

Printed in England

Cover photo shows a pasteurisation system designed by Monsal Limited and commissioned by Binnie, Black & Veitch for Thames Water and is reproduced by kind permission of Monsal.

# CONTENTS

## SLUDGE DIGESTER MIXING AND HEATING SYSTEMS

## SLUDGE MANAGEMENT

# FOREWORD

*Dr Roger King*
*Chief Executive*
*BHR Group Limited*

Since privatisation in 1989, the water and sewerage providers have been under increasing and sometimes competitive pressure from regulators, legislators, shareholders and the general public. Against this background, it will be appreciated that the provision of services which ensure quality, safety and profitability, and which simultaneously comply with environmental legislation is no mean task.

In this time the structure, ownership and management of the service providers have undergone huge changes. Further changes are inevitable, as the industry competes for investment with the non-regulated sector, sheds its local government image and becomes in effect driven by private sector imperatives. This is manifest by the separation of ownership and operation of assets, in a bid to reduce the cost base and reduce risk.

Following initial concentration on improving drinking water quality and reducing leakage, attention has shifted to sludge, firstly as a result of environmental pressures and secondly as the next target for cost reduction. Perhaps because of the recent changes, the industry is less averse to change, and is increasingly receptive to the adoption of innovative and proven practices and processes relating to sludge generation, treatment, handling and disposal

This conference has two main themes: the overall management of sludge and heating and mixing systems for sludge digesters. Both are directed at the requirement to reduce costs and improve profitability whilst satisfying environmental legislation. The papers describe some of the novel and available opportunities applicable to all stages of the sludge cycle, and I feel sure that the volume will become a standard reference on these topics.

# SLUDGE DIGESTER MIXING AND HEATING SYSTEMS

# The application of fundamental rheological and mixing studies to provide energy efficient mixing of anaerobic digesters

Dorian Harrison[t], Colin Brade[t], Mick Dawson[‡], Jacquie Christodoulides[‡], Martin Tillotson[*]

[‡] BHR Group Limited, [t] Monsal, [*] Yorkshire Water Services

## ABSTRACT

There is a scarcity of fundamental work on the mixing of municipal sewage sludge as applied to anaerobic digestion and other treatment processes. Most design is based on "rule of thumb" and other non-rigorous methods. R&D has generally focused instead on measuring the performance of existing installations using chemical tracing techniques. Whilst this provides some comfort for operators, it in no way allows for optimisation of mixing system design with respect to sludge properties, solids content and digester shape. A collaborative research project was undertaken by BHR Group on behalf of Monsal and Yorkshire Water to address some of these issues.

## 1    INTRODUCTION

The lack of fundamental research into mixing anaerobic digesters stems largely from the difficulty of working with materials such as sludge, which vary in properties from day to day and from site to site. A collaborative research project between BHR Group, Yorkshire Water and Monsal aimed to characterise digested sludge rheology and investigate the effect of sludge rheology, digester geometry and mixing system design on mixing performance at both laboratory and pilot scales. Some of the findings from the rheology survey and laboratory scale work have been published[1,2]. The results from the rheology survey enabled an improved correlation for prediction of digested sludge rheology to be developed.

The performance of two unconfined gas mixing methods (sequential and simultaneous), two liquid jet orientations, and an impeller system were investigated and compared in terms of blend time and active volume. The blend time was the time taken to blend a tracer into the actively mixed region of the digester and the active volume was the size of this actively mixed region. The systems were compared at equal net power inputs, that is the power input to the sludge rather than the power input taken from the power rating of the compressor, jet pump or impeller motor. The electrical efficiencies of these different systems vary and should be taken into account when performing a cost analysis of the different systems in terms of CAPEX and OPEX. However, for the research work, direct comparisons were required in terms of the power input to the sludge.

The sequential gas mixing arrangement produced the largest active volume at the lowest power input and one of the shortest blend times. There was a strong correlation between viscosity and the active volumes and blend times for all mixing systems, although the sequential gas arrangement showed the least effect. The findings of the unconfined gas mixing studies were somewhat unexpected, and a second phase of work is ongoing to allow more precise optimisation in the application to full scale. This paper provides a résumé of the unconfined gas mixing work to date, and in particular focuses on the application of the research findings to three full-scale plants - a total of 19 anaerobic digesters. The paper also discusses the various mixing options available to designers, and compares them in terms of CAPEX and OPEX and ease of application to new and existing plants. The authors also consider the overall mixing energy implications from the mixing, heating and feeding systems and their importance in arriving at an integrated energy efficient solution.

## 2    FUNDAMENTALS OF DESIGN

Like many aspects of design within the wastewater industry, gas mixing of anaerobic digesters has been based on experience and "rule of thumb" methods. So long as digesters were operated at 4 to 5% dry solids feed and 20 days retention, the only detrimental consequence of this philosophy was excessive power consumption.

However, with digesters typically being operated at 12 days retention time with thicker feed sludges and guaranteed retention times, active volumes, minimum temperature and pathogen reduction, these criteria are no longer sufficient to design a suitable mixing system.

There are many factors that must be considered when optimising a digester and several of these are directly influenced by mixing.

Uniform dispersal of the feed sludge allows the whole biological inventory within the digester to be fed regularly and equally. This also allows the first stages of digestion - hydrolysis and acidogenesis - to take place evenly across the digesting mass.

Maintaining an even temperature profile within the digester is essential to maintain high rate digestion throughout the active volume and to ensure the biomass operates within a stable environment.

Effective mixing will also avoid concentration of inhibitory agents and volatile fatty acids (VFA's) in any one area. Dispersion of VFA's evenly throughout the digester will improve the methanogenesis phase of digestion and reduce the likelihood of foaming.

Good mixing will maintain operational volume and minimise short-circuiting, making sure the retention time of sludge is maximised. This is increasingly important as regulation and commercial representations demand audited minimum retention times and levels of pathogen reduction.

Once a designer understands the objectives of a mixing system, it is then essential to understand the fluid being mixed. Digesting sludge is a non-Newtonian, three-phase, shear-thinning fluid, as will be discussed in Section 3.1.3.

# 3    MODEL DIGESTER STUDIES

## 3.1    Data collection

Due to limited information on full-scale digester geometry, operation and sludge properties, a survey of 17 digestion sites within the Yorkshire Water area was undertaken. The results from this survey were used to design a laboratory scale model digester and to select a liquid simulant with similar rheological properties to those measured for a range of digested sludges.

Results from this survey are presented in Table 1. Records were not always complete and the dashes indicate where this was the case.

The unconfined gas gross power inputs (P/V) were determined using compressor power ratings and assuming 100% efficiency. The net power inputs were determined using the isothermal expansion of the rising gas plume:

$$P = \dot{n}RT \ \ln\left(\frac{p_1}{p_2}\right) \qquad\qquad \text{(Eqn.1)}$$

Where  $P$ = power input (W)
  $n$ = molar gas flow-rate (mol/s)
  $R$ = universal gas constant (J/mol/K)
  $T$ = temperature (K)
  $p_1$ = pressure at nozzle
  $p_2$ = pressure at sludge surface.

The net P/V values are approximately one third of the gross P/V values suggesting a compressor efficiency of about 30%.

### 3.1.1    Digester geometry

Most of the digesters surveyed had shallow conical sloping bases with an angle of 7° or so whilst two had a steeper slope of 20°. The majority of digester inlets were located at the top by the wall, two inlets were located in the base by the wall and one was situated centrally at mid-depth. All of the outlets were overflow weirs positioned at the top of the digesters. In some cases, the inlet and outlet were positioned close together which could result in short-circuiting of the feed sludge.

### 3.1.2    Digester operation

The majority of the digesters surveyed were fed on a semi-continuous basis, with a frequency of several minutes per 20 to 30 minute cycle. The feed sludge usually entered the recirculation loop where it was preheated to the digesting sludge temperature.

The method of gas addition for the unconfined gas injection digesters varied. The gas was either supplied in a pre-arranged sequence to each diffuser for a set period or was supplied simultaneously to all of the diffusers. Gas could also be supplied continuously or intermittently throughout the day, the latter case being the preferred method within the surveyed digesters.

**Table 1: Survey findings from 17 Yorkshire Water digestion sites**

| Site | Mixing System | Aspect Ratio | Vol. (m³) | Mixer geometry | Gross P/V (Wm⁻³) | Net P/V (Wm⁻³) | Digested Sludge %DS |
|------|---------------|--------------|-----------|----------------|-------------------|-----------------|---------------------|
| A | Unconfined gas | 0.94 | 530 | 8 diffusers in outer ring 4 diffusers in inner ring | 6.7 | 2.2 | 3.4 |
| B | Unconfined gas | 1.2 | 728 | 8 diffusers in outer ring 4 diffusers in inner ring | 4.2 | 1.4 | - |
| C | Unconfined gas | 0.53 | 4900 | 16 lances | 10.5 | 3.5 | 3.7 |
| D | Unconfined gas | 0.93 | 4586 | 24 diffusers in two rings | - | - | - |
| E | Unconfined gas | 0.85 | 1130 | 8 diffusers in outer ring 4 diffusers in inner ring | 5.7 | 1.8 | - |
| F | Unconfined gas | 1.08 | 3500 | 9 diffusers in base | 12.9 | - | 2.5 |
| G | Unconfined gas | 1.07 | 1540 | 8 diffusers in outer ring 4 diffusers in inner ring | 4.2 | 1.7 | - |
| H | Unconfined gas | 0.92 | 565 | 8 diffusers in outer ring 4 diffusers in inner ring | 5.6 | 1.5 | - |
| I | Unconfined gas | 0.9 | 2276 | 18 around the base | 2.8 | 0.9 | 3.1 |
| J | Unconfined gas | 0.53 | 5670 | 1 ring of diffusers in base and at mid-depth | - | - | 3.3 |
| K | Unconfined gas | 0.4 | 105 | 12 diffusers in the base | - | - | 5.0 |
| L | Unconfined gas | 0.82 | 1005 | 24 diffusers in the base | 3.1 | 0.9 | 2.4 |
| M | Unconfined gas | 0.84 | 2920 | 8 diffusers in outer ring 8 diffusers in inner ring 1 central diffuser | 7.8 | 2.1 | 4.6 |
| N | Unconfined gas | 0.81 | 500 | 1 ring of diffusers in base | 8 | - | 3.3 |
| O | Confined gas | 0.41 | 10280 | | 2.5 | 0.5 | 4.0 |
| P | Confined gas | 0.36 | 3400 | | 8.8 | 1.0 | - |
| Q | Mechanical mixing & sludge recirculation | 0.51 | 4038 | | - | - | 2.4 |

### 3.1.3 Sludge rheology

Samples of sludge were withdrawn from each of the digesters surveyed and their rheological properties measured. Sludges exhibit non-Newtonian behaviour where the shear rate and shear stress do not vary proportionally as for a Newtonian fluid such as water. Due to the different composition of sludges, their rheological behaviour varies between sludge types and between sites. Samples of 22 digested sludges from different sites were taken to provide a more complete understanding of their rheologies, and ultimately, to help select suitable simulants for use in the laboratory.

### 3.1.4 Rheology measurements

Brookfield LVDV-II+ and DVIII rheometers were used in the 'open-sea' condition where the spacing between the cup and bob is wide enough to avoid the effect of solids suspended in the sludge[3].

The rheological properties were determined by performing linear regressions on the shear stress-shear rate data and fitting to the Herschel-Bulkley model:

$$\tau = \tau_y + k\dot{\gamma}^n \qquad\qquad \text{(Eqn.2)}$$

The effect of digesting high dry solids sludges was investigated in this work. The surveyed digested sludges ranged from 2.5 to 5% DS. To provide thicker sludge samples a 10%DS sludge was formed by evaporation in an oven at 35°C. Three sludges (2.5% DS, 5% DS and 10% DS) were chosen as representative of the surveyed range of sludge rheologies and are shown in Figure 1.

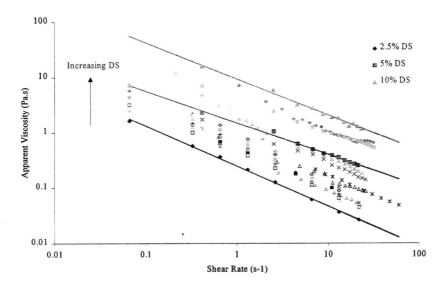

**Figure 1: Range of apparent sludge viscosities found from site survey**

It can be seen that the increase in apparent viscosity between 2.5% and 5% DS is an order of magnitude. Similarly, the increase in apparent viscosity between 5% and 10% DS is an order of magnitude further.

### 3.1.5 Simulant selection
A simulant was required for each of the three representative sludges of 2.5%, 5% and 10%DS. The simulant needed to be durable, easy to make-up and use, transparent for flow visualisation, non-hazardous and cost effective. After trying several types of polymer solutions, Grade 7H4C CMC (sodium carboxymethylcellulose) was chosen for use in concentrations of 0.3%, 0.6% and 1% by weight. Figure 2 shows the viscosity v. shear rate data for these simulant concentrations with the corresponding data from the sludges being simulated.

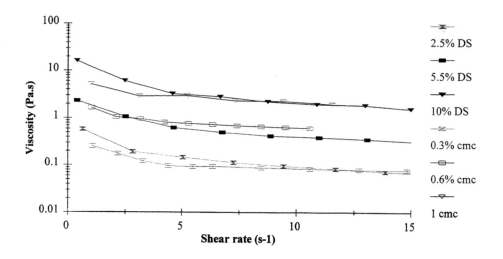

Figure 2: Comparison of Sludge and Simulant apparent viscosities

A laboratory scale model digester was designed to reflect the vessel and mixer geometries found during the site survey. The result was a 0.61m diameter cylindrical Perspex vessel, with a flat base. In addition, a pilot scale 2.67m diameter cylindrical vessel was used for a number of tests.

### 3.2 Model digester for unconfined gas blending

Two gas sparger arrangements were investigated and are shown in Figure 3. Sparger A consisted of a central ring of 4 diffusers with gas supplied simultaneously to all 4, this represents a system found commonly in practice. Sparger B consisted of a central ring of 4 diffusers and an outer ring of 12 diffusers with air supplied to each diffuser in sequence.

### 3.3 Experimental Methods

A range of gas flow-rates was used for the two unconfined gas sparger geometries to give net power inputs per unit volume spanning the range of values found on-site.

#### 3.3.1 Blend time determination

The rate of liquid blending can be determined by measuring the time taken for the concentration of a tracer material to become uniform throughout all of the test volume. Here a salt tracer (NaCl solution) was used to follow the rate of blending. The tracer was added to the vessel and its concentration measured using 5 miniature conductivity probes. The blend time experiments were conducted in a batch feed manner with the tracer inlet and volume matched relative to those found during the site survey. It soon became clear that the responses of the probes in different regions of the model digester could vary significantly. This indicated that fully turbulent flow was not present throughout the model under all test conditions. Visual observation clearly showed the extent of 'active' and 'inactive' zones. Probe responses in the 'active' zones agreed well, leading to the adoption of an 'active' zone blend time. All the blend time results presented in this paper are for the 'active' zone.

#### 3.3.2 Active volume determination

Flow patterns were recorded using a combination of dye and flow followers (neutrally buoyant coloured plastic shapes). Visual observation and video footage were used to determine the approximate size and locations of both 'active' and 'inactive' zones in the model digester. Both active volume and blend time results are presented in the next section.

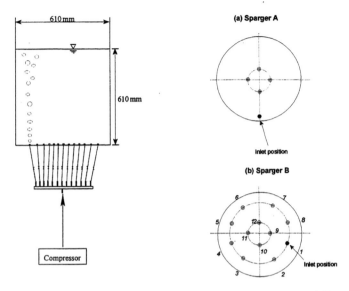

Figure 3: Unconfined gas injection with Spargers A and B

## 3.4    Results and discussion

Figure 4 compares actively mixed volumes using continuous (Sparger A) and simultaneous (Sparger B) unconfined gas addition. The sequential addition of gas through nozzles distributed across the digester floor resulted in a much larger actively mixed volume than simultaneous gas addition at equal net power input in simulants equivalent to sludges of 2.5% to 5%DS. As expected, increasing sludge thickness from 2.5%DS to 10%DS significantly reduced the actively mixed volume whereas increasing net power input increased active volume.

Figure 5 is a representation of the actively mixed volumes observed using Sparger A. The last regions to become active were around the circumference of the digester base. As viscosity increases or power input falls the actively mixed volume shrinks until it forms a narrow cylinder around the gas plume rising from the four centrally placed nozzles. Sequential gas addition through a larger number of well-spaced nozzles prevents the formation of persistent stagnant or 'inactive' zones.

The blend times measured in the actively mixed volumes using unconfined gas spargers A and B are shown in Figure 6. The blend times for the two sparger types were similar in 0.3% CMC (simulating approx. 2.5%DS digested sludge). However, as the simulated sludge thickness increased, the sequential gas addition (Sparger B) provided active volume blend times that were significantly shorter at equal net power input. It was also evident that as sludge thickness increased not only did the active volume shrink but the blend time within it also rose.

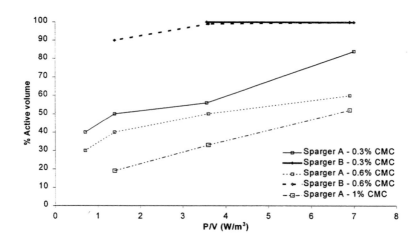

Figure 4: Percent Active volume Vs P/V for unconfined gas spargers A and B

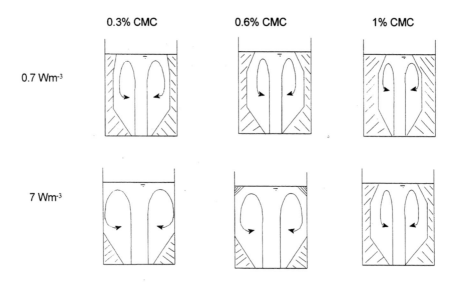

Figure 5: Representation of active volumes for Sparger A

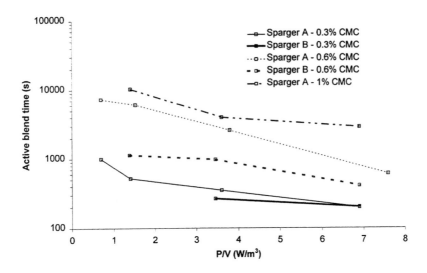

**Figure 6: Active blend time vs. P/V for unconfined gas spargers A and B**

During the experimental work[1,2], it became apparent that using a traditional central ring of diffusers with simultaneous gas addition was inappropriate for thicker sludge. At the pilot scale, it was observed that as the apparent viscosity of the sludge increased, the active volume reduced and a 90% active volume could not be achieved, irrespective of power input. Figure 7 shows the experimentally derived active volume model applied to a digester 10m deep, 14m in diameter with an 8%DS feed, mixed by a central ring of diffusers at 1/3 radius.

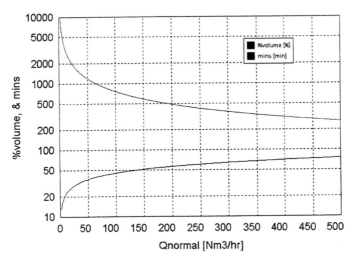

**Figure7: Active volume and blend time comparisons for a digester with 8% DS**

It can be seen that even with a gas flowrate of 500 Nm³/hr, the digester will only be 75% mixed and will reach 90% active volume with a gas flowrate of 980 Nm³/hr. A similar model with a feed of 10% DS reaches an asymptote at an active volume of 82%.

This example shows that the sludge dry solids, and by implication rheology, is a prime factor in selecting the mixing system employed. By comparison, a sequential gas mixing system would require only 300 Nm³/hr to fully mix an identical digester at a dry solids feed of 8%.

The most effective unconfined gas mixer in 0.3% and 0.6% CMC was the sequential gas Sparger B both in terms of blend time and active volume. Tests have yet to be carried out at the lower end of the power-input range for this sparger to see whether this is still the case.

It has been shown that understanding the rheology of the fluid to be mixed is essential, but what rheological data do we use?

The only industry standard prediction method is to use the Water Research Centre (WRc) TR185 report[4] to predict viscosity for an upper, a median and a lower bound. Figure 8 shows the comparison between the measured rheology of a digested sludge and that predicted from TR185.

As can be seen, the actual data for the sludge is considerably different to that predicted by TR185 whereas the Herschel-Bulkley model closely matches the experimental data.

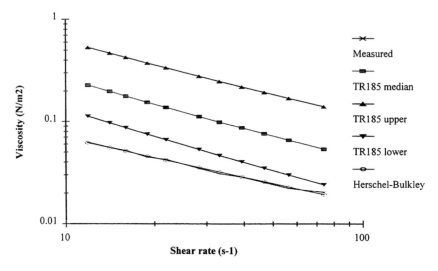

**Figure 8: Log-log plot showing comparison of apparent viscosity - TR185 predicted and measured for a 4% DS digested sludge**

The approach that the partners have taken is to produce a mixer-sizing model that incorporates rheological data, either taken from measurement or predicted using the yield stress prediction model produced within this project. Both approaches have been used in the case studies that follow.

Finally, we need to consider the digester geometry that will be mixed. The research programme was based on two aspect ratios of 0.5:1 and 1:1 using a vessel with a flat base. A shallow digester with a low aspect ratio proved much harder to mix than a tall digester with a high aspect ratio.

In applying the mixing model to actual digesters with steeper floor slopes of say 30° such as that of Mogden WwTW (Thames Water), it is often necessary to calculate the effect of each mixing point individually.

Other factors to take into account are the digester feed and draw-off points, frequency and rate of feeding.

## 4. ENERGY AND PROCESS ADVANTAGES OF SEQUENTIAL MIXING

The fundamental approach adopted in the development work provides a better understanding of how sludge rheology affects mixer performance and can thus be used to improve the design of real plants.

Phase 1 of the research undertaken by the authors showed clearly that for thick sludges, sequential gas and impeller mixers provides best performance. The second phase of work, now underway, will further refine the design process so that the full potential of sequential gas mixing is realised in all sludge mixing applications.

In many plants sequential gas mixing offers additional benefits over other mixing systems in that the design can be individually tailored for each application. This is achieved by varying the gas flows, diffuser numbers, their location and the pattern of sequencing to ensure complete mixing of the digester irrespective of internal geometry and sludge rheology.

This infinite adaptability coupled with simple retrofit to existing digesters has led the authors to favour the sequential gas mixing system for real world applications. Three case studies are presented below which show how the high efficiencies achievable with this system can significantly reduce energy costs without compromising performance.

Mixing energy used in all digester systems is, by comparison with conventional process applications, extremely low and great care is needed in design especially with thick sludges. It is recommended that designers adopt an integrated systems approach to digester mixing with consideration being given to all mixing energy inputs including those resulting from feeding, heating, gas generation and natural buoyancy forces. Further details of this approach are given in the following case studies.

### Case Study 1: Rayleigh WwTW, Anglian Water

| | | |
|---|---|---|
| Digester Volume | - | 1076 m³ |
| No. Digesters | - | 1 |
| Design Feed solids | - | 8% DS |
| Date of installation | - | 1998 |

The challenge on this scheme was to provide a mixing system for a thick sludge high rate digester with average feed solids concentrations of 8%. The initial proposal was to install an unconfined gas mixing system using conventional simultaneous gas injection arranged using diffusers on a one third PCD of the digester diameter. The design basis for this approach is entirely empirical, based on experience.

The early findings of the research project were used to develop a revised design, which incorporated sequencing of the gas injection in order to increase the certainty of achieving full digester active volume with this very thick sludge.

This early design split the mixing system into two independent sections allowing each half of the digester to be mixed alternately, at full power. The design was flexible so that by linking both sections a conventional simultaneous mode of operation was also available. The control system was designed to allow variation of input power to match actual feed sludge solids so that energy would not be wasted in the event that sludge concentration was less than design.

On this plant the feed position was altered, such that raw sludge was introduced into the digester heating recirculation loop, the diffuser layout was optimised to disperse the feed sludge and the mixing cycle was interlocked with the feed pattern. This ensured that all mixing energy inputs worked together rather than against each other, a situation found all too often in digesters in which the process systems have not been integrated.

The energy savings obtained by switching to a sequential mixing pattern are shown in the table below. Based on simultaneous mixing power requirements versus sequential mixing requirements and assuming 24 hour operation, 365 days per year and a power cost of 4p per kWh.

| Mixing System | Simultaneous | Sequential |
|---|---|---|
| Power Consumption (kWh/pa) | 105120 | 65700 |
| Cost (£/pa) | £4,205 | £2,628 |

The sequential system shows a saving of £1,577 p.a. in energy costs compared with the simultaneous option.

### Case Study 2: Mogden WwTW, Thames Water

| | | |
|---|---|---|
| Digester Volume | - | 4100 m$^3$ |
| No Digesters | - | 16 |
| Design Feed solids | - | 7.5% DS |
| Date of installation | - | 2000 / 2001 |

On this very large site the client required a highly efficient mixing system to minimise energy costs. Various systems were considered and only sequential gas mixing could provide the power savings without compromising mixing performance and be easily installed in these existing digesters with their gas bell roofs.

The brief was to develop a mixing system tailored to the existing digesters at Mogden to allow the feed regime to be increased to 7% dry solids with a minimum retention of 12 days. This new feed regime would then allow the decommissioning of 4 out of 20 digesters.

In this scheme predictive rheology using the Herschel-Bulkley model was the basis of the final design and this allowed the mixing performance to be predicted.

Even with a full design model now available from Phase 1 of the research project, the design was not straightforward. The steep slope of the floor and the disadvantageous aspect ratio, necessitated the mixing system be calculated on a point by point basis, with several mixing point geometries investigated.

Feed to the digesters is batched approximately every 4 hours and is pre-heated before entry to the digester. Design blend time was based on 2 hours allowing full dispersion of feed before the next batch.

As with Rayleigh WwTW, an integrated approach to the process inputs was adopted with all energy inputs being considered and their contributions combined. This integration of the mixing, heating and raw feed heating is thought to be the most advanced in the country.

The table below compares a conventional simultaneous mixing system based on the client's standard of 8 $W/m^3$ installed power with the actual power consumption used by the sequential gas mixing system.

| Mixing System | Simultaneous | Sequential |
|---|---|---|
| Power Consumption (kWh/pa) | 247908 | 73584 |
| Cost (£/pa) | £9,916 | £2,943 |

The sequential system shows a saving of £6,973 p.a. in energy costs compared with the simultaneous option. Over the total of 16 digesters this gives an estimated saving in energy costs of £111,567 pa.

### Case Study 3: Aberdeen WwTW, East of Scotland Water

| | | |
|---|---|---|
| Digester Volume | - | 4000 $m^3$ |
| No Digesters | - | 2 |
| Design Feed | - | Hydrolysed raw sludge, 12% DS |
| Date installed | - | 2001 |

Aberdeen WwTW is in a green field site development funded by a PFI (Private Finance Initiative). The PFI consortium building the plant is also responsible for running the plant for 25 years and is particularly keen to reduce energy and maintenance costs. The flowsheet is based on Cambi pre-treatment followed by mesophilic anaerobic digestion and this is designed for very high feed solids concentrations typically 12% DS. This combination of high feed solids coupled with a need to minimise power use led to the client selecting the Monsal sequential gas mixing system which could be designed using the available rheological information from similar plants.

Rheology data provided by the main contractor is shown in Figure 9. These parameters were input into the mixing model derived in the stage one research. This approach allowed an optimised solution to be designed to meet the client's needs.

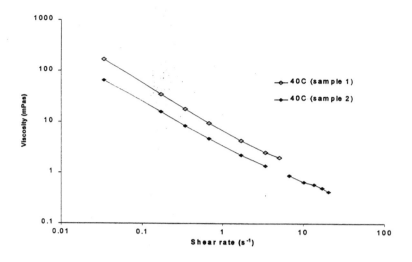

**Figure 9: Rheology data for hydrolysed sludge**

During the design, as in the other case studies, an integrated energy input approach was adopted with particular attention paid to dispersing this thick feed sludge. Hydrolysed sludge enters the digester at 40°C and there is considerable danger of an 'inactive zone' developing as the hot feed accumulates on the surface. This problem also occurs in conventional digesters and has been shown to result in a high acid concentration zone in the digester and serious foaming and other operability problems including untreated sludge short-circuiting to the digester outlet.

The client specified a design power for mixing of 8 W/m$^3$, which would have resulted in an installed compressor size of 32 kW. A comparison of the energy consumption for the sequential system with the original specification based on 8 W/m$^3$ can be seen below.

| Mixing System | Simultaneous | Sequential |
|---|---|---|
| Power Consumption (kWh/pa) | 251412 | 132276 |
| Cost (£/pa) | £10,056 | £5,291 |

The sequential system shows a saving of £4,765 p.a. in energy costs compared with the simultaneous option. Over the total of 2 digesters this gives an estimated saving in energy costs of £9,530 pa.

## 5    CONCLUSIONS

Most digesters in the UK currently use unconfined gas mixing systems with net power inputs of 1.5 to 3.5 W/m$^3$, a majority of these systems feature simultaneous rather than sequential gas addition. At equal net power inputs with well-spaced diffusers, the manner in which gas flow was introduced into model digesters had a very significant impact on the size of the actively mixed volume and blend time within the actively mixed volume. By switching the total gas flow from one diffuser to the next in the sequence considerably greater active volumes and shorter blend times could be achieved when compared with continuously dividing the total gas flow between all the available diffusers. The superiority of the sequential gas arrangement increased as the sludge dry solids content and hence viscosity increased. In addition, the sequential gas addition system provided greater actively mixed volumes which is becoming increasingly important with new controls over pathogen content and the need for guaranteed residence times.

In addition, many new sludge treatment methods are coming into use and this coupled with a clear trend for digesters to be operated with much higher feed sludge solids concentrations exposes the designer to significant risk of process failure when traditional "rule of thumb" design methods are used.

The fundamental mixing studies undertaken by the authors has provided a set of predictive models which use sludge rheological properties and actual digester geometry to provide a more certain method of ensuring the required mixing regime is achieved.

The most effective mixing arrangement for a digester can only be achieved by adopting an integrated energy approach in which all potential mixing energy inputs, including feeding, heating and buoyancy forces, are considered. Mixing systems designed using these methods have been selected for 19 digesters and the case studies provide details of these applications.

The research studies predict significant energy savings are possible with sequential mixing systems.

A second stage of research is now underway and this will further refine the design process so that the full potential of sequential gas mixing is realised in all sludge mixing applications.


6    REFERENCES

1.    Dawson M., Christodoulides, J., Fawcett, N. and Brade, C. "A Comparison of Mixing Systems in a Model Anaerobic Digester" *5th European Biosolids and Organic Residuals Conference, Aqua-Enviro, Wakefield, UK.* 19-22 Nov. 2000

2.    Barker, J., Dawson, M. "Digester Mixing: Theory and Practice" *3rd European Biosolids and Organic Residuals Conference, Aqua-Enviro, Wakefield, UK.* 16-18 Nov. 1998

3.    Whorlow,R.W., Rheological Techniques, Ellis Horwood Ltd., 1980.

4.    Frost, R. C. "How to Design Sewage Sludge Pumping Systems" Technical Report TR185, Water Research Centre, 1983

# Draft tube sludge mixer –
# a unique solution for the process of digestion

*Erik Lahner [1], Uwe Werner [2]*

[1] *Manager of Business Unit – Multistage Pumps and Mixers, Sterling SIHI GmbH*
[2] *Product Manager of Business Unit – Mixers, Sterling SIHI GmbH*

Abstract:

Since the 1950s, there has been a constant increase in water consumption and the amount of wastewater. Municipalities and industries are forced to treat sewage more and more intensively. The anaerobic digestion process is a common way to reduce the organic ratio in the sludge by generating useful methane gas. The anaerobic organisms used in the conversion of waste solids to methane are very sensitive to changes in process conditions. Therefore, homogeneous mixing is essential for a uniform temperature and nutrient profile. A reliable and economical system is required to solve problems in large tanks such as deposits at the bottom and the formation of scum and foam on the sludge surface.

This paper describes the concept of the draft tube sludge mixer which circulates the sludge upwards or downwards through a vertical tube. This mixing system controls foaming, eliminates scum and supernatant sludge layers on the surface, prevents solids deposits at the bottom, mixes the digester contents intensively and maintains a uniform temperature profile to provide optimum conditions for bacterial growth. The mixer can be used in any digester – cylindrical, cylindrical-spherical or egg-shaped.

## 1    Introduction

In mechanical process engineering, a sludge mixing system consists of a mixing device and the digester. A successful digestion process in the digester, with a satisfactory gas yield, a sufficient reduction of volatile suspended solids (VS) and short retention times depends on the suitability and efficiency of the mixing system. One of the main principles to observe when selecting the digester shape is that an optimal relationship between cylindrical height (H) and diameter (D) should be achieved.

In any homogenisation process a D/H ratio of $\geq$ 1 should be aimed at. The lower section of the digester should preferably be conical and have a flat bottom.

In most cases, however, the digester shape will depend on local circumstances (e.g. ground structure, spatial restrictions, etc.) and economic aspects. Thus, especially in the event of upgrading an existing digester, a mixing machine would be desirable which can be successfully used in a large variety of digester shapes.

As early as the 1930's the draft tube sludge mixer was developed by the German company MAN. This mixer meets the special digestion process requirements in large digester types. It has been used in all common digester types, from the ideal egg- shaped digesters (termed ESD) to the flat storage tanks preferred in the USA in the past.

This paper summarises the first results of experience gained in 172 sewage treatment plants (STP) around the world, where a total of 300 draft tube sludge mixers made by Sterling SIHI GmbH (formerly Halberg Maschinenbau GmbH) have been installed. In also includes literature contributions. Eighty per cent of the information provided in this paper reflect knowledge gained over the past 10 years.

## 2    Anaerobic digestion mixing systems

If the digestion process is found to be unsatisfactory, the likely reason is inadequate and inefficient mixing of the digester contents, resulting in dead zones where no mixing takes place, in the build-up of supernatant sludge layers and foam and deposits at the disgester bottom. The digestion process is constantly impaired and the desired sludge stabilisation and gas production can only be achieved by increased retention times.

The requirements a mixing system should meet in order to ensure optimal anaerobic digestion can be described as follows:

1. The complete digester contents need to be homogenised with the raw sludge supplied in a continuous process.
2. Intensive mixing is required to maintain a sufficient exchange of substances.
3. Avoidance of temperature and material gradients.
4. Efficient utilisation of the entire digester volume.

A number of different mixing systems are available to meet these requirements. There are four established systems:

1. Draft tube sludge mixer
2. Agitators
3. Gas injection systems
4. Recirculating pump systems.

These systems produce similar mixing results, but they vary greatly with regard to specific power consumption (P/V), mode of operation and undesirable effects, such as the formation of scum or deposits.

One of the advantages of the draft tube sludge mixer is its capacity to reverse operation, thus counteracting the formation of scum or supernatant sludge layers. At the same time, this mixer type is a very compact and reliable machine.

Agitators need to be carefully designed, as the operating limits are narrowed by the rotor or shaft diameter and the length of the shaft.

In gas injection processes, the gas generated is supplied to the digester through several lances or ring nozzles. The digester contents are thoroughly mixed by the upward flow. However, heavy particle deposits cannot be prevented. In many cases, it is necessary to clean the digester at regular intervals.

In a recirculation system, sludge is pumped from the lower digester area to the digester top. This operation is reversible, but the mixing results are not satisfactory. Moreover, as with gas injection, the power consumption level of this mixing system is very high. It is frequently used as an additional mixing device whose main function is to pump the sludge through an external heat exchanger.

## 3    Draft tube sludge mixer construction

The draft tube sludge mixer is a vertical rotatary pump, which allows no direct comparison with agitators. Basically, it consists of two components - the mixing equipment, including shaft and the pumping device, and the draft tube. The pumping device is inserted and adjusted in the special upper draft tube bellmouth. The sludge is pumped at a velocity of 3 m/s upward or downward through the draft tube.

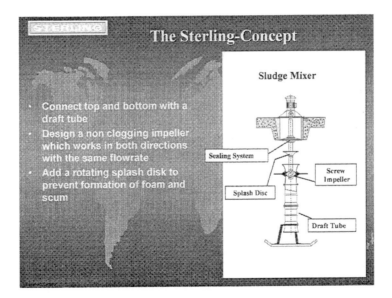

## 3.1    Draft tube

The draft tube connects the two critical digester zones where the requirements are particularly demanding.

The danger in the upper zone is that a supernatant sludge layer and scum may build up and even reach the gas bleeder lines. The lower zone is a potential area for the accumulation of heavy solids contained in the primary sludge pumped from the sedimentation tank into the digester. Such deposits can considerably reduce the reaction space within the digester and lead to costly cleaning measures.

The draft tube is installed on a robust base structure. Lateral stability is achieved by four horizontal bracing ropes. In order to avoid vibration, long draft tubes are additionally braced in the middle. In the event of rope failure, the remaining three ropes will still secure the correct position of the draft tube.

## 3.2    Pumping device and splash disc

The overhung mixer shaft has a (one- or two-stage) pumping device and a splash disc mounted to it.

The pumping device consists of two opposite helical blades and is adjusted within the upper draft tube bellmouth. The clearance between blade edge and digester wall is a few millimetres. Even in the case of the largest draft tube sludge mixers with a flowrate of 7,200 m³/h the clearance does not exceed 15 mm. These small gaps allow a very efficient pumping performance. The pumping device is self-cleaning, i.e. even large plaits, which despite screens and grinders sometimes get into the interior of digesters, cause no problems.

The splash disc has been developed and optimised over several decades. During upward operation, it diverts the liquid flow to the sludge surface. The splace disc distributes the sludge over an area of a diameter of up to 4,500 mm.

## 3.3    Mode of operation

The operation of the draft tube sludge mixer is reversible, i.e. the sludge can be moved upward or downward.

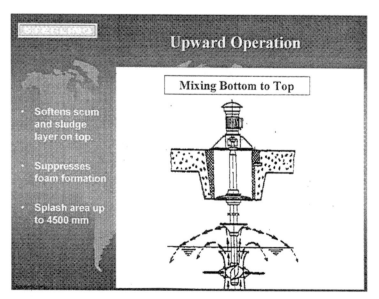

During upward operation, the splash disc distributes the sludge over the sludge surface area softening the supernatant sludge layer and destroying part of the scum built up during the process.

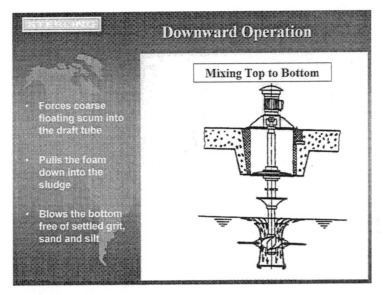

During downward operation, the softened supernatant sludge layer and the scum will be sucked down the draft tube and remixed with the digester contents. The high velocity of up to 3 m/s causes a strong jet flow at the lower bellmouth, flushing away any deposits at the bottom.

Reversible operation ensures the problems in the critical zones are successfully dealt with and the digester contents are thoroughly mixed.


## 4 Digester shapes

There are various digester shapes, e.g. egg-shaped digesters (ESD), conical-cylindrical-conical shapes used as standard in Germany, and flat storage tanks which were the preferred solution in the United States.


## 4.1 Cylindrical storage tanks

Flat cylindrical storage tanks used as digesters have a height-diameter ratio of H/D < 0.5. The bottom is flat and the ceiling is flat or slightly conical, which is why this tank is sometimes referred to as "pancake". The digester contents are mixed by several gas lances or a gas lifting system in combination with a recirculating pump system. As in other digesters, the sludge is heated to the desired process temperature by steam injectors and/or external heat exchangers.

This digester shape used in conjunction with gas injection will give unsatisfactory results. Thus, in many cases, an efficient digestion process is not possible. Moreover, the successful destruction of pathogenic microorganisms required for the generation of Class A biosolids is less than assured in digesters of this type.

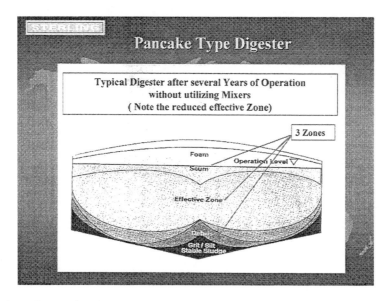

Regular and expensive cleaning is necessary to remove deposits, which reduce the digester volume. A possible solution would be an over-sized digester so as to provide suffient reaction space over an extended period of time. However, the mixing tasks would become much more demanding.

The draft tube sludge mixer has been successfully used several times in such flat tanks. The effect of the unfavourable height-diameter ratio has been neutralised by the installation of up to three mixers. Due to the intensive jet flow at the lower draft tube bellmouth, deposits can be prevented in all areas of the digester. It is also possible to control the formation of scum.

An economic analysis is necessary for this mixing system consisting of a flat tank and multiple draft tube sludge mixers. Calculations must not only reflect the low purchase price of a flat tank, the low operational costs of draft tube sludge mixers and the improved process performance (e.g. increase in gas production) but also the high investment cost incurred by purchasing more than one draft tube sludge mixer.

## 4.2   Conical-cylindrical-conical digester

This is the standard digester type in Germany. It is conical towards both ends (gradient approx. 25°) and a cylindrical central section. The H/D ratio is ≥ 1. This shape may be described as a modification of ESD. The ESD principle (slender shape, tapered bottom and top) is realised using simple structures. In order to minimise costs a flat bottom is often used instead of a cone. However, if the digester volume is 5,000 m³ or larger, the construction of the upper section is very expensive and ESD is the better alternative.

This digester type can be equipped with many different types of mixing equipment, from gas mixing systems, through agitators to draft tube sludge mixers. Gas mixing systems are commonly used in France and the Benelux countries. Scandinavian operators prefer agitators and in Germany the draft tube sludge mixers are the preferred and well established solution.

According to plant operators, draft tube sludge mixers have been successfully used in both conical-cylindrical-conical shaped digesters and ESD.

About 12 per cent of this type of digesters equipped with draft tube sludge mixers have a flat bottom. This digester shape has been developed over the past 10 years, probably as a result of increasing cost pressure.

The flat bottom is unfavourable to the mixing process, but there is no evidence of a reduced mixing effect of the draft tube sludge mixer. Model tests have shown that the flow is sufficient even in the outermost digester bottom areas. The dead zones are surprisingly small and reduce the effective volume by less than 1%.

## 4.3   Egg shaped digester (ESD)

The egg shape is ideal for the use of draft tube sludge mixers. Egg-shaped digesters taper towards the bottom leaving just a small area for deposits of heavy solids. The liquid surface in the gas area is also relatively small. In this area, foam forms quickly generating thick layers which may even reach the gas line. It is vital that the formation of scum and foam is counteracted. In many systems the mixing process is supported by a closed circular pipeline for steam injection in the outside digester diameter.

ESD digesters account for about one third of all digesters equipped with draft tube sludge mixers. These digesters are relatively large and their volume is 7,800 m³ on average. ESD's having a volume of at least about 5,000 m³ are generally considered to be an economical choice. However, 33 per cent of the ESD's investigated are digesters with a volume of less than 5,000 m³. It can be assumed, therefore, that this general rule is no longer applicable and even smaller ESD digesters can be successfully used.

The jet flow generated by the draft tube sludge mixers effectively prevents solids from settling in the digester tip. The formation of foam in the gas chamber is largely controlled by reversible mixer operation. The contents in all areas of the digester are homogenised. This has been proved in a tracer test on a 11,000 m³ ESD (Back River STP, Baltimore, USA).[1]

Combining draft tube sludge mixers with ESD is an ideal solution. This is underlined by successful applications in sewage treatment plants, for example at Back River (2 x ESD, each having a volume of 11,000 m³), Hyperion, L.A. (18 x ESD, 9,500 m³), Yokohama (10 x ESD, 6,800 m³) and Emschermuendung, Germany (3 x ESD, 16,700 m³).

## 5   Experience

In the past 70 years more than 700 sludge mixers of the type described above have been installed and successfully used in a large variety of digesters worldwide. However, it is only now that a systematic survey including the accumulation of the sewage treatment plant operators' data and information relating to draft tube sludge mixers has been started. The information given in this paper represents the first results of this survey. It will be updated on a regular basis.

## 5.1    Homogenisation characteristics

The homogenisation characteristics of mixing systems can be determined by means of a lithium tracer test, i.e. a tracer is introduced into the mixing system and its time-related concentration in different areas is recorded. The results are then compared with theoretical models describing the size of a dead area, etc.

Such a test has been conducted at the Back River sewage treatment plant in Baltimore. The mixing results of two ESD's (2 x 11,356 $m^3$) have been compared, one of the digesters has been equipped with a draft tube sludge mixer and the other with a gas injection system. The mixing results have been good in both cases, but the gas injection system consumed three times the energy required by the mixer.[1]

The Back River sewage treatment plant is currently being expanded, and the fact that, unlike gas injection, the draft tube sludge mixer allows mixing in either direction will be one of the important factors to be taken into account.[2]

Reports received from the sewage treatment plant at Cologne-Stammheim (5 x ESD, 11,000 $m^3$ each) have also been positive.[3]

## 5.2    Settling characteristics

One of the key advantages of the draft tube sludge mixer is the generation of a jet flow which during downward flow removes deposits at the digester bottom. This has been confirmed by operators of different digester types.

The jet flow is sufficient to homogenise sludges with a total solids content of up to 10%. If, however, an excessive amount of sand gets into the digester, the mixing process will break down. If the deposits reach the draft tube it appears that the sand pile keeps falling back until it clogs the tube causing the mixing operation to collapse.

## 5.3    Supernatant sludge layer

In the past, it has been one of the main tasks of the draft tube sludge mixer to destroy supernatant sludge layers. In the meantime, screens installed upstream from the sedimentation tank have proved a successful means of preventing the formation of such layers. The original mixer operation, upward operation during 50% of the time to destroy the supernatant sludge layer and downward operation during the other 50% to suck down scum and foam and prevent the formation of deposits has been changed to a ratio of 20 % - 80 % to suit the new operating conditions.

## 5.4 Formation of foam and scum

The digestion process produces gas which is primarily methane (60%). This two-phase system (liquid/gas) inevitably produces foam. Additional gas sources, such as, for example, gas injection, will lead to a considerable increase in the formation of foam. The stability of the foam depends on the viscosity of the sludge and the presence of further microorganisms, which increase foam stability. For example, filamentous bacteria, such as microthrix parvicella, are thought to create significant quantities of foam. This has been observed only recently and appears to take place mainly in autumn and winter.[4][5]
Moreover, the process control itself is a frequent cause of increased formation of foam. The conventional mesophilic digestion process has been found to be the reason for the foam and scum problems in two-thirds of all sewage treatment plants in the USA which treat activated sludge.[9]

As any other system, the draft tube sludge mixer can only minimise foam build-up, not prevent it entirely. The modified operation using 80% of the operating time to pump the sludge downward effectively counteracts the formation of foam.

Even a short-time stop of the mixer at the Oldenburg STP in Germany produces foam to an extent which is hard to control. Using the draft tube sludge mixer again, it is possible to reduce this amount considerably.

## 5.5 Gas production

The production of gas depends primarily on sludge quality and the process used. The selection of the mixing system plays a minor role in this respect.[6,7]

Tests conducted at the Yokohama sewage treatment plant (10 x ESD, 6,800 m$^3$ each, equipped with draft tube sludge mixers) have shown that in a single-stage mesophilic digestion process a gas amount of about 23 m$^3$ per 1 m$^3$ of sludge is generated in a period of 30 days. The process is assumed to be limited by the rate of flow of the raw sludge, and the potential of bacteria producing methane is believed to be significant. Again, it is vital that the raw sludge and the digester contents are effectively homogenised.[8]

Thermophilic processes lead to an increase in gas production rate by 30 to 100 per cent, thus reducing the retention time. This method is very susceptible to temperature and concentration gradients and depends on a particularly reliable mixing process.[9] The gas injection method is assumed to have a negative influence on gas production reducing perfomance by 10%.[10]

## 5.6 Retention time

The retention time depends on the process control rather than on the mixing system. It can be reduced from about 24 to 30 days to 12 days by changing over from single-phase to two-phase process control.[7] Appropriate homogenisation of the digester contents is necessary to ensure satisfactory process control.

## 5.7    Specific power consumption

The specific power consumption of mechanical mixing systems is very low. The draft tube sludge mixer imparts 2 to 3.5 $W/m^3$ to the sludge, agitators about 2 $W/m^3$ and gas injection systems up to 6 $W/m^3$. Intermittent operation offers additional savings potential, as in many cases it will be sufficient to circulate the digesters contents 4 to 6 times per day. [1,11]

## 6    Conclusion

The first results have shown that the draft tube sludge mixer has proved highly successful in all common digester types. For example, an unfavourable H/D ratio has been compensated by multiple mixer installation. Experience indicates that the ideal mixing system is a combination of draft tube sludge mixer and ESD.

The problems in the two critical zones of a digester are solved by the special features of the draft tube mixer and reversible operation. Effective homogenisation of the digester contents, the main task of the mixing system, is ensured. The specific power consumption of the mixer is low.

The draft tube sludge mixer meets the application demands of modern two-stage digestion processes and helps achieve the aims of an increase in gas production and a reduction of the retention time.

# 7 Literature

[1] G.G. Balog, L.S. davis, A.S. Sokhey, G.B. Heiner, J.M. Holland; "Evaluation of Egg-Shaped Digester Mixing by Tracer Methods at the Back River Wastewater Treatment Plant, Baltimore, MD";

[2] G. Winfield, A. Sokhey, R.B. Schroedel, T.E. Wilson, J.J. Martx; "Innovative Digestion at Baltimore"; WEFTEC 2000

[3] J. Oles; N. Dichtel, H.-H. Niehoff; "Full Scale Experience of Two Stage Thermophilic / Mesophilic Sludge Digestion"; Wat. Sci. Tech.Vol. 36, No. 6-7, pp 449-456, 1997

[4] A. Dillner Westlund, E. Hagland, M. Rothmann; "Operational Aspects on Foaming in Digester caused by Microthrix Parvicella"; Wat. Sci. Tech. Vol. 38, N0. 8-9, pp 29-34, 1998

[5] P. Madoni, D. Davoli, G. Gibin; " Survey of Filamentous Microorganisms from Bulking and Foaming Activated-Sludge Plants in Italy"; Wat. Res. Vol. 34, No. 6, pp. 1767-1772, 2000

[6] M.H. Wong, Y.H. Cheung; "Gas production and Digestion Efficiency of Sewage Sludge containing Elevated Toxic Metal", Bioresource Technology 54 (1995), pp 261-268

[7] S.K. Bhattacharya, R.L. Madura, D.A. Walling, J.B. Farrell; "Volatile Solids Reduction in Two-Phase and Conventional Anaerobic Sludge Digestion"; Wat. Res. Vol. 30, No. 5, pp 1041-1048, 1996

[8] Y.Y. Li, O. Mizuno, T. Miyahara, T. Noike, K. Katsumata; "Ecological Analysis of the Bacterial Systems in a Full-Scale Egg-Shaped Digester Treating Sewage Sludge"; Wat. Sci. Tech. Vol.6; No. 6-7, pp 471-478, 1997

[9] Yue Han, Shihwu Sung, R.R. Dague; "Temperature-Phased Anaerobic Digestion of Wastewater Sludges"; Wat. Sci. Tech. Vol. 36, No. 6-7, pp 367-374, 1997

[10] T.E. Wilson, N.A. Dichtl; "Two-Phase Anaerobic Digestion: An Update On the AG Process"; WEFTEC 2000

[11] Fa. Oswald Schulze GmbH & Co.KG; "Process technology of sludge digestion"; company journal

# Tank mixing with the Rotamix process

*Richard Behnke*
*Senior Product Specialist, Vaughan Company*

## Abstract

The Rotamix technology has been successfully proven in anaerobic digesters, sludge storage systems and sludge blending tanks feeding dewatering equipment along with numerous other applications in the wastewater industry. These applications have consistently provided significant power and operational cost savings.

The Rotamix systems operational versatility, low scheduled maintenance requirements and significantly lower capital costs have made this system one of the fastest growing technologies in the wastewater and bio-solids handling markets.

## Introduction

The Rotamix system consists of a pump external from the tank, which recirculates flow form the process through an arrangement of nozzles located on the floor of any tank geometry. The system has proven to be effective on either conical or flat floor designs. The quantity of nozzle assemblies is determined by the tank size and the size of the nozzle assemblies is determined by the mixing energy provided to assure maximum effectiveness within the process for which the system has been designed. There are significant alternative equipment applications and sizing options, which enhance the versatility of this system even further.

The system has been applied in anaerobic digesters, sludge storage tanks, equalization basins, aerobic digesters, lime stabilization processes, sludge blending tanks, anoxic zones.

This technology is also currently in design stages with application in several CSO projects for the prevention of solids sedimentation and accumulation, which would reduce the holding capacity of the CSO system.

## System Outline

A typical system would be comprised of a pump external of the process for which it is being applied. The minimum quantity of nozzles assemblies is two with no limit on the maximum.

However, for a general guide, there are six assemblies typically associated with a tank diameter of 110 feet (33.53 meters). The exception to the two-assembly minimum is for tanks with a diameter of 35 feet (10.66 meters); in those applications the use of one mixing assembly is acceptable.

Each assembly consists of cement lined ductile iron piping serving as the main header. Attached to each assembly header is a Rotamix nozzle head. (**Please refer to figure 1.**) Each nozzle head is manufactured with a Brinell rating of 450 to protect each unit from the affects of abrasion especially during continuous duty.

One of the advancements made with regards to nozzle design has been the improvement of terminal energy created by the nozzle length. Typically the transition into the main acceleration zone has been very short. This form of design offers a disadvantage with regards to terminal discharge energy due to a turbulent flow condition being created within the nozzle, which allows the fluid to rotate, and at discharge is actually more of a spray discharge rather than a tight plume discharge. The nozzle heads associated with the Rotamix system have a significantly longer transition into the acceleration zone which hydraulically provides a much tighter discharge pattern from each nozzle head. This ultimately leads to a significant increase in terminal mixing energy for each nozzle assembly.

**Figure 1**

The effect of the spray discharge has shown to have a significant impact on the discharge continuation energy supplied through a nozzle assembly, thus having a significant impact on the distance a particular fluid will travel before the effects of gravity and subsequent reduction in velocity affect the mixing energy available within a process.

The next part of the system is the pump applied which serves as the method from which the contents of the process are recirculated through the nozzle assemblies. The pump typically used with sludge applications or other processes where solids of fibrous materials are present is a chopper pump. This form of pump allows for material to pass through the system at a size, which prevents maintenance issues with the pump or the nozzle assemblies. This pump has also proven to prevent the reweaving of fibrous materials, which often present a problem with regards to stresses on typical rotating equipment. A significant maintenance benefit of this system is that there is **no** scheduled maintenance within the process.

However, there are process applications where this form of pump is not necessary and other types of centrifugal pumps can be used. These applications would include, but not limited to, ground water storage, alum sludge storage and lime slurry storage tanks.

**System Operation**

One of the key problems facing engineers and operations mangers with regards to mixing is the prevention of solids from collecting within the middle 60% of any process. This typically has been defined as the "tea cup affect".

This condition is created when the rotation of a fluid forces solids to the center of the tank due to a low-pressure condition within the middle 60% of a particular process. This condition creates several significant issues related to operation and maintenance.

The most significant of these issues is the inconsistent solids concentrations throughout a particular process. This condition has a dramatic impact on the operation and performance of processes such as digesters and sludge blending tanks, which rely on maximum efficiency created from consistent concentration levels of solids either for proper solids reduction or optimizing the thickening process and subsequent chemical consumption associated with the sludge dewatering process.

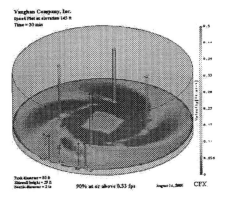

**Figure 2**

The application of the dual nozzle approach per mixing assembly allows for the focus of a substantial amount of mixing energy within the inner 60% of a particular process in addition to providing enhanced mixing energy distribution to the upper regions of a particular process. The energy focus in the lower regions of a process allows for a significantly faster rotation near the center thus creating higher-pressure zone within this area, which ultimately prevents solids from being able to accumulate in the middle of the tank. The distribution of mixing energy through the elevated nozzles allow for proper energy distribution with regards to terminal mixing energy at the surface which has a dramatic influence on the development of typical scum formation issues.
**(Please refer to figure2 and figure 3).**

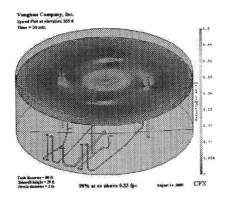

**Figure 3**

The unique nozzle design also provides additional mixing energy through induced flow. The principle of the nozzle design creates a headloss and subsequent velocity at the nozzle discharge, which creates a condition where fluid is actually induced into the flow pattern at a rate of approximately 4-6 times that of the actual nozzle discharge rate. This is very important to the system performance when being considered for mixing applications in anaerobic digesters.

**Specific Process Operational Examples**

**Sludge Storage**

This form of mixing technology was originally introduced in the sludge storage market. It quickly caught the attention of engineers and operators alike because of its unique ability to effectively operate on an intermittent basis.

The system allows for any sludge storage tank to be filled and left unmixed for periods of 6-8 months. Then when the time comes for disposal of the sludge the system typically operates for 3-5 days to suspend organic and inorganic solids to a differential percentage of 10% of the mean concentration level. In actual performance the system usually suspends the settled material in approximately the first 12-14 hours. This method of operation not only saves operational costs, but also allows for the decanting of excess water from the tank to reduce the amount of liquid handled by a facility on an annual basis.

This form of mixing has provided hundreds of installations with obvious substantial operational. The following table illustrates just such a scenario. The community had been mixing their sludge storage tank with a conventional approach, but they were accustomed to having that system operate 24 hours per day. This technology was applied and the pump operated for 12 days per year. The first set of mixers consisted of 2 motors rated at 10 horsepower. The Rotamix system used a 25 horsepower pump. The electrical cost was 7.5 cents per kilowatt-hour.

| Mixers | | Rotamix | |
|---|---|---|---|
| Motor Qty. | 2 | Motor. Qty. | 1 |
| System Hp. | 20 | System Hp | 25 |
| Total hours Per Year | 8650 | Total Hours Per Year | 12 |
| Cost per KW/Hour | 7.5 cents | Cost per KW/Hour | 7.5 cents |
| **Annual Operating Cost** | **$1210.00** | **Annual Operating Cost** | **$21.00** |

Another significant advantage with this technology is the ability to integrate additional tanks into a one-pump scheme. In addition it has proven to be very effective in using the mixing pump to also operate as the system transfer pump to either an application vehicle or dewatering equipment.

42

**Anaerobic Digesters**

With the experience gained from the area of sludge storage, a significant advancement in anaerobic digester mixing has materialized.

During the design process engineers have always evaluated a systems ability to produce a desired turnover rate within a particular digester. The Rotamix technology has led the way in an innovative approach to determining the necessary mixing energy for an anaerobic digester. Once the relationship between the pumping rate and total volume is calculated a mixing energy factor is determined which will produce a minimum 90% active mixing rate in less than 30 minutes. The system is designed to provide simultaneous energy dispersion throughout the digester simultaneously through all the nozzle assemblies, which allows for the high active mixing rates within the digester in a very short period of time. This achieves the same process criteria for high rate digestion that is achieved with other methods yet offers **installed** cost savings between 25% and 60% of what it normally costs for just the **initial** purchase of other technologies.

**Process Testing**

The following table provides data, which was gathered in a field test using Lithium Chloride to trace the effective mixing, produced by the Rotamix system. The test was performed on an anaerobic digester with 5% sludge being fed from a gravity belt thickener.

The analytical procedure was preformed with Inductively Coupled Plasma-Mass Spectrometry. A series of discreet samples were taken to determine the background lithium levels. The lithium solution was then injected into the digester to produce a 5% concentration.

A series of discreet samples were then taken from three separate sampling points. The first sample was taken 3 feet from the floor and subsequent samples were taken every 6 feet thereafter. This procedure was the same for all sampling points.

The specifications required that the samples be within +/- 10 % of the mean value, which for this test location was .0813 ppm.

With the mean value at .0813 ppm. The differential ratio needed to be between a maximum value of **0.8943** ppm and **0.7317 ppm**.

| Sample ID | Lithium Value |
|-----------|---------------|
| A! | 0.86 |
| A2 | 0.88 |
| A3 | 0.89 |
| A4 | 0.78 |
| B1 | 0.76 |
| B2 | 0.87 |
| B3 | 0.86 |
| B4 | 0.77 |
| C1 | 0.77 |
| C2 | 0.87 |
| C3 | 0.78 |
| C4 | 0.77 |

The results from this test were very similar to another set of results where the same test was preformed on a digester at the same facility.

## Conclusion

Although not having a significant name recognition at this time. The author of this paper believes that this form of mixing offers the most dynamic improvement in this area of sludge handling that has been presented in years. The proven mixing efficiency, initial capital cost savings, minimal scheduled maintenance and operational flexibility this technology should lead in the field of solids mixing for years to come.

# A comparison of advantages and disadvantages between different sludge mixing systems in digester tanks

*Nick Peck*
*The Utile Engineering Company Limited*

This paper sets out to briefly highlight various methods of sludge mixing and to provide a brief indication of the advantages/disadvantages and implications of the use of different methods.

## 1.    SLUDGE MIXING

This is part of the treatment process of sewage where thickened sludge contained in digester tanks of varying shapes, sizes and materials, needs to be mixed as effectively and efficiently as possible, in order to comply with the UK Code of Practice for Mesophilic Anaerobic Digestion.

There are many methods of mixing with varying degrees of efficiency aimed at producing a homogeneous mixture within the digester tank, between partially treated sludge and undigested raw feed sludge aimed to promote primarily:-

- Even temperature throughout the tank
- Growth of bacteria to aid the breakdown of sludge
- The reduction in levels of volatile organic compounds

Different methods of mixing also have varying effects on the following:-

- Grit deposition at base of digester
- Scum formation on the top of sludge
- Breakdown of sludge
- Production rate of Methane gas

With efficient mixing, coupled with maintaining an even temperature within the digester of $35°C$ +/- $3°C$, further benefits include reduced retention time and increased availability of methane gas produced which can be utilised in boiler or CHP applications rather than being released to atmosphere, or flared off.

## 2.     DESIGN CONSIDERATIONS FOR DIGESTER TANKS & MIXING SYSTEM

- Insulation
- Aspect ratios of 1.0 to 1.1 between diameter and depth of tank
- 3 dimensional screening to reduce ragging and fibrous material in sludge
- Sloping floor to base of digester
- Heating method
- Foaming
- Gas draw off
- Method of mixing
- Capex
- Maintenance and whole life costs


## 3.     METHODS OF SLUDGE MIXING

### 3.1     Gas Mixing
Over many years, several methods of gas mixing have been tried, tested, and used in various sectors of the Water Industry, all having varying degrees of effectiveness. Some of the same systems have different names, and others are simply variations on a theme.

### 3.1.1   Gas Injection
Gas is taken either from a separate gas holder or directly from the top of the tank and re-introduced to the bottom of the tank following compression.

- Direct, either by leaf spring diffuser at the centre base of digester or via lances feeding down from digester roof
- Direct into the side of the digester wall
- Sequential, using any of the aforementioned

### 3.1.2   Mechanical Mixing
An early method of mixing sludge by having a propeller shaped blade submerged within the sludge and capable of rotating in either direction, to provide an uplift or downdraft effect. These often require a separate blade near to the top level of the sludge for use as a scum breaker.

- Standard blade on shaft driven by motor on roof
- Housed in a tube drawing sludge in at one end and pushing it to the other vertically

### 3.1.3   Pumping
Pumping sludge from the top of the digester either directly or taken from an overflow box and injecting towards the base of the tank generally tangentially, has been used for many years, however, this has an increased power requirement as the Dry Solids Content increases.

# 4. BENEFITS AND DISADVANTAGES OF DIFFERENT METHODS OF MIXING

## 4.1 Gas Mixing

### 4.1.1 Advantages
- No moving parts within digester
- Simple to install
- Easy to maintain
- Elevated gas temperature improves overall efficiency

### 4.1.2 Disadvantages
- Regular service requirements
- Small carryover of oil

## 4.2 Mechanical

### 4.2.1 Advantages
- Lower maintenance costs
- Quick installation

### 4.2.2 Disadvantages
- Ragging and blinding of blade/paddle
- Intolerance to increase in % dry solids
- Lack of standby facility
- Poor indication if mixing system fails
- Prolonged downtime in event of failure

## 4.3 Pumping

### 4.3.1 Advantages
- Simple
- Easy to control

### 4.3.2 Disadvantages
- High power requirements
- Fouling of pumps
- Poor mixing

# 5. CAPEX

Installation costs vary between different methods of sludge mixing, however, the capital costs between each method may work out to be very close in order to achieve effective mixing. Many varying factors can affect the installation costs, some key issues being:-

- % of dry solids within sludge
- Tank volume
- Tank design
- Method of mixing being considered

It must also be pointed out that no matter how effective a mixing system is, many other factors will have an important part to play in the effective digestion of sludge. One such factor is heating. Although gas temperature is increased in gas mixing systems as a result of compression, giving an increase in overall efficiency of the system, supplementary heating is necessary. For reduced capex, a heating system capable of maintaining a sludge digester working temperature should be considered with the possible need for supplementary heating, via emergency steam injection for example, when starting from cold is necessary. Careful sizing is required and calculations should take into account worst case scenarios and possible contingencies.

## 6.    MAINTAINANCE & WHOLE LIFE COSTS

Very often, an important issue when assessing various methods or proposals for mixing in general, is; whole life cost. By adding maintenance costs over a fixed term to motor running costs, the whole life cost can be evaluated. However, the overall efficiency and effectiveness is often overlooked. A system with a lower whole life cost should not be considered if any of the main criterion for mixing are not achieved.

Furthermore, unexpected breakdowns, or the need to remove plant for service, are not taken into account. Where moving equipment is located within the digester tank posing hazardous situations and may require de-commissioning of the digester tank.

## 7.    CONCLUSIONS

Different methods of sludge mixing with different designs of tank, coupled with old and unreliable/unsuitable equipment, means that many existing systems are not operating at their maximum potential. Running costs are also excessive for older systems.

With advances in technology, better understanding, availability of more reliable, more suitable and more efficient equipment, means that vast improvements can be made in the efficient treatment of sludge. Further environmental and economic pressures should drive the need for a refurbishment programme to be undertaken.

The most economical and cost effective solution for whole life and capital costs, should see the utilisation of unconfined direct continuous gas injection via sliding vane compressors, where injecting gas towards the bottom centre of digesters has become the most popular.
Sequential gas mixing increases capital and maintenance costs, compounded by limited life cycles of solenoid valves. Higher costs are also associated with more complex PLC control of solenoid valves in sequential mixing.

When making any final assessment including whole life costs, it is important to bear-in-mind the technical back-up and service that can be provided by equipment manufacturers and sub-contractors, along with down times and subsequent consequences should breakdowns occur.

# Practical aspects of sludge pumping systems for digesters

*D Hucknall, M Lancett*
*Hidrostal Limited*

SYNOPSIS

This paper is presented to show how an apparent simple pumping operation has become difficult and unpredictable by process changes, restrictive specifications, the effect of large ranges of sludge concentration and different blends of sludges.

Changes are discussed along with the ways they have effected the pump selection and how we, as a pump supplier, have responded to these changes.

The authors examine a number of sites that have had difficulties, discuss what the problems were and the corrective measures needed for the system to operate as intended.

The paper shows how small changes can have major effects and how very small changes sometimes make the difference between a digester heating system working or not working.

The authors also discuss the use of pumps for digester mixing, based on worldwide applications and advise that the technical arguments raised in this paper regarding the design of pumping systems for sludge heater re-circulation duties, apply equally well to the designs of pumped digester mixing systems and sludge tank mixing systems.

## 1    INTRODUCTION

This paper has been written based on the extensive field experience of the authors and draws attention to the fact that the characteristics of sewage sludges have changed dramatically in recent years which have many implications for the pump supplier.  The main items discussed are:-

♦ How the digestion process has changed
♦ How these changes have effected the pump selection
♦ How, as a pump supplier, we select and supply pumps to meet the performance required for a system.
♦ Examination of a number of sites to discuss the problems, the reason for these problems and how they were solved.
♦ Information required by the pump supplier for proper pump selection.

- The specifications for pumps currently used by the water companies.
- Pump mixing and typical systems.

**Figure 1 Typical sludge heating system**

## 2    CHANGES TO THE DIGESTER PROCESS

The water industry has been using digesters for many years and until recently the mixing and heating system has rarely been a problem. The pump duty was easy to calculate and the pump supplier would be confident that the system would perform to expectations.

In recent years the sludge being digested has changed from just a primary sludge to a sludge that is now one of the most difficult materials to handle. It has high solids contents, can be a blend of various sludges, is viscous and can contain large quantities of gas. To make things even more difficult, large percentages of poly-electrolyte thickened surplus activated sludge can be present, along with quantities of rag and grit. These mixtures of sludges are producing much larger quantities of gas than the older digesters and sludge retention times have been reduced to as little as 12 days with modern high rate digesters. Some processes are digesting large quantities of surplus activated, sludge sometimes up to 95% SAS which presents major problems regarding pump selection. The major problems being extremely high gas concentrations and high viscosities.

### 2.1   Effect of changes

The effect of these changes for the pump supplier is that the selection of the pump is more difficult, particularly when most pump specifications ask for the pump having a dry solids content (DSC) varying between 4 - 8% and with no indication of type of blend or the sludge to be pumped.

50                          © BHR Group 2001 Sludge

## 2.2 Effects on pump selection

To be able to match the pump with the system requirements it is important to know the mixture of the sludge blends and what the sludges' solids contents are in the digester, and not the widespread of the solid content of the feed material, it needs to be more precise. Figures 2 and 3 show the effect of a typical sludge pump specification with a large range of solid contents.

## 3 VARIATIONS CAUSED BY A WIDE SLUDGE SPECIFICATION

### 3.1 Methods used for flow loss calculations

Within the UK it is normal to use Technical Report No 185 by Russell Frost. The flow loss is calculated using this method but the specification often asks for the pump to handle a sludge ranging from 4.5 - 8% DSC (dry solids content).

In practice these variations hardly ever occur; as a sewage treatment plant having settled down will produce a sludge of a fairly consistent DSC and the system should be optimised for this DSC.

Since a wide range of sludge has been specified it is clear the process engineer anticipates that in extreme circumstances these wide variations can occur. To cater for this eventuality the pump engineer needs to ensure these extremes can be handled by the pump at some other flow rates.

The pipeline friction for a heating system including heat exchanger losses as given in Figure 2 circa 25 l/sec, the head ranges from 9.0m and 39m based on upper bound WRC TR 185 with 4.5% and 8% sludge.

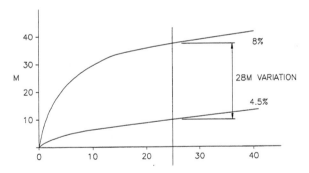

*Figure 2* **Typical system curve TR185 upper band for 4.5% and 8% sludge showing the large variation in friction losses**

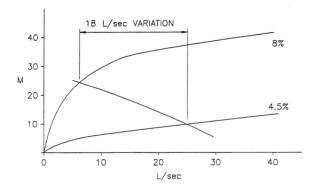

**Figure 3 is Figure 2 with a pump's performance curve showing the variation in pump output for 4.5% and 8% sludge**

### 3.2  Considerations when choosing a pump

Where problems often occur in the field the pump has been selected on price and not technical merit.  They normally comply with water company specifications, ie, speed not exceeding 1500 rpm and with 100mm free passage, with no consideration as to where the duty point is on the pump's performance curve.

It is the authors' experience that it is often more important to select a pump which is non compliant to specification in order to guarantee reliable system operation.  This often means using speeds in excess of 1450 rpm and free passages less than 100mm.  The benefit of this is normally a pump with a significantly higher shut off head thereby providing a greater pressure reserve to cater for larger solid variations.

### 3.3  Badly selected pump

The pump shown in Figure 4  was selected on price and not on technical merit.  This was replaced by a smaller, faster running pump with a steeper performance curve and its duty point near the best efficiency point  (BEP).

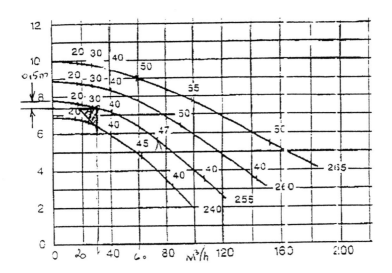

*Figure 4* **Poorly selected pump**

The curve is too flat, the duty point is too far on the left hand side of the curve, with virtually no reserve in head between duty point and closed valve head.


**3.4    Best pump for the job**
Frequently the pump that does not comply to the sewage pump specification is far better on sludge heating systems. Running them at 2900 rpm or other speed by using belt drive, or similar, the duty point can be selected near the best efficiency point, reducing operation costs, lower wear rate and often it is less expensive to purchase.

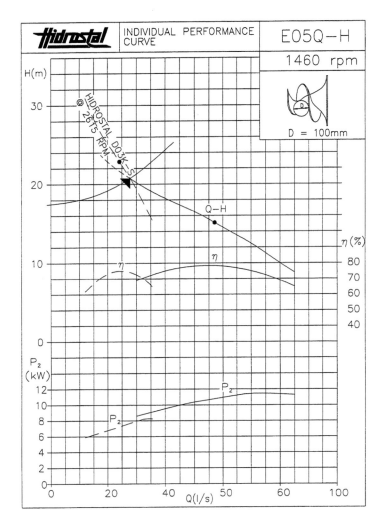

*Diagram 5* **Comparison between 1450/2900 shows the advantage of a smaller, faster running pump showing a steeper Q & H curve**

## 4  ADDITIONAL PROBLEMS WITH MODERN HIGH GAS PRODUCING DIGESTERS

### 4.1  Main problem
a)  The effect of the gas on the pump's ability to generate pressure
b)  Gas collecting at a high point in the system and "gas locking" the system or the pump.

### 4.2  Effect of a gas rich sludge
The effect of a gas rich sludge is on the suction of the pump. The gas bubbles that are present in the sludge expand rapidly in the suction pipe as they approach the pump, due to the drop in pressure in the suction pipe due to the flow friction losses or the loss of static head if the pump is located above the take-off point of the digester.

This is followed by the collapse of the gas bubbles as they pass through the impeller. This will affect the ability of the pump to generate pressure and modifies the pump's performance curve. It affects all types of centrifugal pumps, particularly conventional sewage and multi vane types. The screw centrifugal impeller pump by virtue of its screw type semi-displacement inlet section does not suffer in the same way and is ideally suited to handle this difficult material provided it is selected correctly. Although it is not a NPSH problem as there is usually at least 10m positive head on the pump, it effects the impeller in the same manner as cavitation.

## 4.2 Importance of low suction pipe losses
Because of the gas bubble problem, the suction side engineering is most important. The losses must be kept low and the best place to install the pump is close to the digester. Use the minimum number of fittings, short length of pipe and avoid high points.

## 4.3 Unscreened sludge
If the sludge contains rag and a macerator is to be used, install it in the sludge feed pipe, so that all solids entering the digester are reduced in size. The macerator can then be smaller, and only runs for a shorter time than if it is installed in the sludge heating pipe, and it will not affect the circulation pump. This removes a major flow loss from the suction of the continuously running recirculation pump.

## 4.4 Sludge feed to the digester
Ideally the sludge feed, should not be connected to the sludge heating system. If this has to be the case, it should be fed into the suction side of the circulation pump, not the discharge This is because the sludge feed pump is normally a positive displacement pump and when they discharge into the circulation pipe it demands the pipe space at the expense of the centrifugal circulating pump increasing the risk of gas locking of the circulation pump and pipe work.

## 4.5 Pipe velocity
A relatively high velocity should be aimed for on the selection of pipe size. This is to reduce the risk of gas collecting at high points of the pipe work. A velocity of 1.5 - 1.8m/s is a good starting point. However, the suction size may need to be larger, to keep the suction loss as low as possible.

## 4.6 Getting the pipe size right for the circulation
The higher velocity will reduce the viscosity which will reduce the rate that flow losses increase. The viscosity also reduces as the temperature rises further reducing the flow losses. So, getting the digester up to temperature is far more difficult than maintaining the digester at its temperature. It will be less costly to run the pump at the digester's design temperature, and if he pump controls allows adjustment in its speed, it can be slowed down reducing the power input to the pump, and the costs to operate the pump.

## 5 THE IMPORTANT FACTORS TO BE CONSIDERED AT THE DESIGN STAGE.

Below are the important points previously discussed in this paper and should be given serious consideration when designing digester heater circulation systems.

♦ Accurate assessment of the sludge

- Accurate assessment of the flow losses
- Correct installation and location of the pump
- Correct pipe size selection
- Low losses on the suction pipework.

## 6    CASE STUDY SITE No 1

Three digesters reach design temperature when commissioned with effluent and then slowly lost temperature as sludge slowly replaced the effluent , followed by failure of the pumps due to wear.

Initial site survey showed that the pumps were installed 30 - 50m from the digester with 100mm dia pipes, the sludge was 45% primary and 55% poly-thickened SAS, and contained grit.

The existing installed pump operated very near closed valve head with only 0.5m in head from specified duty point to the closed valve.

### 6.1    System Assessment
System losses were re-calculated which showed that the head was under specified by approximately 50%. The original pump was never going to work with the specified sludge, although it worked during the initial period of 3 months. This was only because the digester was brought on stream using thin sludge. Thick sludge was slowly added over a number of weeks.    The losses increased and the circulation rate decreased and the digester lost temperature and the existing pumps suffered from premature wear because of internal re-circulation and operation at closed valve.

### 6.2    Sludge Tests

|  | Viscosity k(Pas) | Dry Solids Content % | Wt kg/m$^3$ |
|---|---|---|---|
| Digester 1 | 1.85 | 3.98 | 954 |
| Digester 2 | 1.68 | 4.8 | 930 |
| Thickened SAS | 8.08 | - | 1014 |

Note that this shows that poly thickened sludge is 5 times more viscous than when it is blended with the primary sludge.

Viscosity tests were made on the sludge and the values were used to calculate the flow losses and reproduced the same losses we had calculated by WRC TR 185.

### 6.3    Replacement Pump
Belt driven pumps chosen to replace the existing pumps.  They gave flexibility to be able to match the pump to the system curve by simple belt changes.  Initially these were installed in the heater house in the same position as the original  pumps with long suction pipes, but did not perform very well because of high suction losses. They were re-positioned outside, next to the digester, with very short suction pipes.  This solved the problem and the pumps were

now circulating at the correct rate and the digester temperature increased and after 10 days reached 35°C.

## 6.4     Conclusions

♦ Pump duty incorrectly specified for sludge being handled
♦ Pumps badly positioned
♦ Specifications inappropriate for sludge duties
♦ High suction losses

## 7     CASE STUDY SITE No 2

Pumps were supplied to replace existing torque flow impeller pumps used on the digester circulation that suffered severe wear and blocking problems. The torque flow pumps were fitted to old sludge heater mix units which were replaced with modern heat exchangers.

### 7.1    Solution

New Hidrostal screw centrifugal pumps were supplied and were horizontal mounted V belt driven units rated at 26.0l/s at 7.2m total head. The V belt drive was chosen in order that the pumps could have their duty head increased to 26.0 l/s at 9.6m total head at a later date. this was because when the pumps were first put into service the digesters were running with a sludge of about 2 - 3% dry solids and this would increase when the sludge thickening contract was finished to a sludge of 6 - 7% dry solids. As a result of this increase in sludge thickness, the system head for the pumps would increase and the flow rate would reduce from the required minimum of 26.0 l/s. So a simple pulley change to the pumps would easily bring the installed pumps' performance back to the required minimum flow rate.

When the new sludge thickening plant was in service the sludge did increase to 6 - 7% and the circulation pump's flow rate did fall away from the minimum 26.0 l/s required. The pumps had the pulley change to increase the running speed of the pumps from 1260 rpm to 1450 rpm and this was sufficient to bring the pumps back to the required flow rate.

One problem did start to occur in the form of the pumps and the heat exchanger becoming gas locked on 12 out of the 16 digesters at this site. These 12 digesters were now seeing this new thickened sludge with the remaining 4 digesters seeing only imported green sludge. The thickened sludge now contained about 40 - 50% of 8.5% poly-thickened SAS which was at first believed to be the main problem being light and aerated containing more gas bubbles than normal sludge.

### 7.2    Investigation into the gas locking

Upon further investigation of the whole system the main reason for the gas locking was discovered. The sludge feed into the digester is by two large ram pumps rated at 25.0 l/s giving a combined sludge feed rate per digester of 50.0 l/s. This sludge is pumped into the digester through a branch manifold at between 1.5 - 3.5 hours a day depending on one or two of the feed pumps running. This is also the same manifold used by the discharge of the digester circulation pumps. The result is that when the ram pumps are pumping they prevent the circulation pumps from pumping and this results in a gas build up within the circulation pumps and the heat exchanger, ie, no flow through heat exchanger re-circulation pumps.

Indeed it is possible for this feed sludge to be pumped into the heat exchanger and the circulation pumps in the reverse direction because of no non-return valve in the digester circulation system.

This problem is also exaggerated due to the fact the circulation pumps and heat exchanger are sited at a level half way up the digester with the suction and discharge point for the circulation system at the digester base level so any gas build up in the system will be in the heat exchanger and circulation pump which are located at the highest point in the system.

On all new digesters it is common for the sludge to be taken out near to the bottom of the digester and be returned back into the digester at a high level giving a natural rise to the system. Unfortunately when working on existing digester systems the new equipment has to be installed into the existing pipework arrangement, so it is important to check on what effect the existing system pipework will have on the new equipment being installed.

On new digesters it is normally the case that the feed rate into the digester is much lower than the circulation rate through the heat exchanger system and this feed sludge is frequently fed into the circulation system not direct into the digester. When fed into the heater re-circulation system, it should be into the pump suction pipework not the discharge pipework.

It is most important that the pump supplier be given the whole system details so that they can comment on the system to avoid any potential problems that may arise to prevent the pumps from working successfully.

These details should include the following information:

♦ Pump flow rate and head required
♦ Design sludge thickness to be handled
♦ Full pipework details of the digester circulation system
♦ Raw sludge feed system and flow rate if going into the circulation system
♦ Proposed position of the circulation pump in relation to the digester and heat exchanger

This information is very important to avoid any problems that may occur within the circulation system.

## 8    CASE STUDY SITE No 3

The pumps were supplied against data provided which indicated that the pumps would be handling only normal digested sludge.

The tender specification also restricted pumps to a minimum 100mm free passage and maximum of 1500 rpm running speed. Typical of tender specifications of the time.

This was fairly typical of the type of tender/water authority specification for this application which Hidrostal had been dealing with up to that time. Hidrostal has a large number of pumps installed within all water companies working very successfully on digester circulation that were selected along very similar lines.

## 8.1 Site operational problems

At this site only half the digester is visible above ground level at about 5.8m high. the pumps are mounted duty/standby with individual suction pipe work taking sludge out of the digester at ground level. They both feed into a common discharge main connected to a single heat exchanger and then the discharge main feeds back into the digester at a high level.

It was found that the pumps were very prone to gas locking and they had to be vented by hand on a regular basis. Over a period of time this hand venting was found not to be sufficient to maintain pump and digester performance.

The solution arrived at by site personnel at the time was to tie open the standby pump's non return valve a small way which allowed the duty pump to run for longer periods before becoming gas locked again. This may have promoted some form of re-circulation back to the digester and this, in turn, prevented the pump form gas locking on such a regular basis.

They were also not able to feed the digester at the designed feed rate of 80 m³/day or the gas locking problem would prevent the pump from working at all.

## 8.2 Site inspection report

- ♦ Hidrostal were asked to look at the installation with a view to offering a solution to the problem
- ♦ Pumps were installed vertically as per specification
- ♦ Suction pipe work reduced from 150mm to 100mm diameter using a concentric taper and not a flat top taper in line with good design practice
- ♦ Isolating valves were a plug type which could contribute to turbulence on the pump's suction side allowing gas to come out of suspension within the pump volute
- ♦ The digester contains a mix of raw primary sludge and poly thickened SAS from belt presses on site not pure primary as indicated in the specification.

## 8.3 Recommended action

- ♦ Install a new pump based on the actual site requirements taking into account the type and mix of sludge within the digester
- ♦ Select a pump operating on or near its best efficiency point to match the new calculated duty point
- ♦ Mount the pump horizontally with the pump discharge facing vertically upwards to prevent any gas build up within the pump volute and to minimise suction losses
- ♦ Simplify the feed pipe work from the pumps to the heat exchanger
- ♦ Install one of the originally supplied pumps the same way as the new unit to compare the performance between the two

## 8.4 Action taken

A new pump was supplied on a trial basis and installed in line with our recommendations with the pump mounted horizontally with its discharge pointing vertically upwards. One of the original units was installed as a standby pump and was installed in the same way as the new pump. Both pumps were then connected into a common rising main feeding to the heat exchanger.

The pump trial was for a period of 4 weeks which was felt to be sufficient time to prove the pump and get the digester back up to operating temperature.

## 8.5    Pump trial results

♦ New pump working very well with no gas locking problems
♦ Digester sludge feed rate now up to its maximum of 80m³/day
♦ Digester is now running at the required operating temperature
♦ The original pump installed mounted horizontally showed no improvement and continued to gas lock
♦ The new pump has been ordered along with a second unit to replace the original standby pump
♦ The new pump is very quiet in operation compared to the original units supplied

## 8.6    Conclusions

♦ It is important to supply accurate details of the sludge to be handled to be able to take into account the way that some sludges modify the pump's performance curve.

♦ The design and layout of the pump and pipework are important.  Keep the pipe work simple and pipe runs short, especially the suction side to avoid potential problems.

♦ Take into account the pump supplier's recommendations on such installations as he knows how to get the best out of his product and how to apply it.

♦ A flexible pump arrangement is important so the pump's output can be adjusted to match the heating system requirement and the unpredictable nature of the sludge and possible process changes such as different blends of sludge and thickening methods.  Two options are commonly used:

   i)  Belt driven pumps
   ii) Frequency inverter drives

♦ System flow losses being underestimated and the effect of different sludge thickening processes are not understood.  The pump supplier prefers to be consulted and calculate the flow losses rather than supply  a badly specified pump which subsequently needs to be changed.

♦ Another problem is the pump or the pipe work becoming gas locked.  this again is a greater problem now with the high gas producing digesters.  The usual reason for this is a low velocity in the pipe work.  High points in the pipe work and the use of concentric tapers.

   High points in the pipe work can often be designed out allowing the gas to flow upwards back to the digester with no pockets where it can form large bubbles.  Also a pump selected to operate near its closed valve head and long suction pipes can be a problem.  Getting the velocity right will solve most of these problems and allowing the pump to be operated above 1450 rpm will improve the pump selection.

♦ Generally it has been found that a horizontally mounted pump with a vertical discharge works better than a vertical pump with a horizontal discharge pipe.

- Circulation rate on some problem systems have been solved by straightening the suction pipe and removing any unnecessary bends or changing these to long radius bends, removing restrictions such as small sections of small diameter pipe, changing concentric tapers to flat top tapers, reducing the suction loss and therefore not allowing the gas bubbles to collect and expand as much because of the lower losses.

- Some heating problems have been solved by replacing missing insulation on exposed pipes.

- The circulating pump is only one small part of the heating system, and other important factors also need checking.

  i)   Is the hot water temperature high enough?
  ii)  Is the boiler large enough?
  iii) Has the heat exchanger a large enough capacity to heat the sludge?

## 9   PUMP MIXING OF DIGESTERS

Externally mounted pumps for mixing digesters are seldom used in Great Britain. They are, however, used commonly in the USA and Europe. The comments made regarding the design of pump and heater circulation systems on digesters also apply to the design of pumped digester mixing systems and pump mixer systems on sludge storage tanks.

### 9.1   Advantage of a pump mixing system

i)   A pumped mixing system with an externally installed pump will be easy to maintain
ii)  The pumps will have very large free passages capable of handling all the material of a digester without blocking, Most of the pumps we are likely to supply for mixing have a free passage of 150mm or larger.
iii) Mixing energy can be calculated and varied to suit sludge characteristics
iv)  Can be used on thick sludges and large digesters

**Figure 6 Typical pump mixing system under construction**

Engineers in the water industry in GB in their search to reduce *Life Cycle Costs* (LCCs) of digester mixing systems have come to the conclusion that pump mixing systems utilising a small number of externally withdrawable nozzles presents an attractive alternative to gas mixing and various versions of propeller and draft tube mixers. The fact that all equipment, except the nozzles are external to the digester/storage tank is a very attractive option as regards maintenance.

·A typical pump mixing system is shown in Figure 6 where an old digester was re-used for sludge storage. The photo shows one of two 22kW pumps with twin nozzles immediately prior to being clad with insulation. Site experience has indicated this simple low cost pump mixing system meets fully the operational and maintenance requirements of the water company.

When designing a pump digester mixing and heating system the authors would recommend that the two systems should be integrated so that the sludge which flows through the heating system whilst being a much lower flow rate than that for the primary mixing system could make a contribution to the overall mixing system. By adding on 3 to 5 metres to the head of the heater circulation pump the sludge could be discharged into the digester via a nozzle at a level and direction so as to complement the mixing process.

# What are we achieving with digester mixing?

*Rachel Edgington*
*Severn Trent Water, Alpha House, Warwick*

## ABSTRACT

Over the last few years, lithium tracing has been undertaken on 21 of Severn Trent Water's mesophilic anaerobic digesters to establish the actual retention time, effective volume, the degree of short-circuiting and the time to achieve homogeneous contents within the digester. A representative cross-section of the Company's digesters was chosen having different lengths of time in service, mixing equipment and nominal retention times.

The results show that for the majority of digesters with unconfined gas mixing the effective volume is greater than 80%. Digesters with 'Heatamix' units can be expected to have an effective volume of around 50% after about ten years in service. Short-circuiting was identified in some cases and was found to be a function of inlet and outlet pipework arrangements and/or feeding regimes; preheating of the raw sludge seemed to minimise short-circuiting. The time to achieve homogeneous contents in the digester only exceeds 60 minutes in isolated cases.

## 1. INTRODUCTION

Severn Trent Water has 45 sewage works with mesophilic anaerobic digesters, producing 160,000 TDS/year of digested sludge. In late 1997, there was concern about the adequacy of digestion capacity within the Company and that some of the older digesters may not be operating at their optimum because of increases in sludge production and the build up of inert material within the digester. Hence, it was decided to assess the hydraulic performance of the digesters by lithium tracing. This would also enable the retention time to be checked against the MAFF Code of Practice.

Since the work started, discussions with the British Retail Consortium on the advisability of recycling digested sludge to land have taken place, with particular concern expressed on the level of pathogens in the digested sludge. Poor digester design and operation, especially when short-circuiting is occurring may lead to high levels of pathogens in the digested sludge.

Also, it also has given the Company an opportunity to assess the current design guidelines for digesters, especially the use of unconfined gas mixing which was originally investigated in Severn Trent Water [1].

## 2. LITHIUM TRACING

The objective of the lithium tracing exercise was to establish the nominal and actual retention times, the effective volume and the degree of short-circuiting defined in Figure 1. The exercise also gave information on the mixing time which is defined as the time taken to achieve homogeneous contents within the digester.

Twenty one digesters were traced, the majority being done by in-house staff or outside Consultants. A few were traced as part of Engineering Contracts for newly constructed digesters ( A,B,C,D and F) or after refurbishment of M&E equipment (digesters E and N). Some of the digesters traced were selected because there was some concern with their retention times. There is a wide range of sizes and length of time since they were last empty (either after construction or cleaning) with a variety of mixing equipment installed as detailed in Table 1.

### Table 1 - Digester information

| Digester | Volume (m³) | Time since last empty at test date (yr) | Mixing Equipment |
|:---:|:---:|:---:|:---:|
| A | 1,800 | 1 | Unconfined gas mixing |
| B | 2,350 | 1 | |
| C | 2,700 | 1 | |
| D | 2,800 | 1 | |
| E | 590 | 1 | |
| F | 3,000 | 1 | |
| G | 1,500 | 5 | |
| H | 2,400 | 5 | |
| I | 1,720 | 6 | |
| J | 980 | 6 | |
| K | 2,500 | 10 | |
| L | 2,140 | 12 | |
| M | 2,300 | 1 | Unconfined gas mixing |
| N | 2,690 | 1 | |
| O | 4,700 | 4 | |
| P | 1,800 | 8 | |
| Q | 2,300 | 2 | Heatamix units |
| R | 1,730 | 10 | |
| S | 1,600 | 12 | |
| T | 1,880 | 7 | Bubble gun |
| U | 1,750 | 10 | Burper gun |

All the digesters with unconfined gas mixing, apart from digester J, have a continuous gas flow through the outlet devices (mainly spring leaf diffusers). Digester J is provided with sequential gas mixing with use of a rotary valve. Digesters A to L were purpose built with unconfined gas mixing while M to P have been converted to unconfined gas mixing.

The methodology for tracing with lithium salts was virtually the same for all sites. In nearly all cases, the lithium chloride solution was introduced into the raw sludge line prior to entering the digester, usually downstream of the charge pumps. If the sludge is preheated by the heat exchangers, the lithium solution was injected prior to the heat exchangers. In a couple of cases, the solution was discharged into the roof space close to the cold sludge entry point. Digested sludge samples were taken from the overflow pipework. Sludge sampling consisted of two distinct periods:
• On the first day, immediately after the lithium solution injection, sampling was done every five minutes for the first hour and then every fifteen minutes for the next three hours. The results of this work gave an indication of short-circuiting and the time it takes to achieve homogeneous contents, the mixing time, within the digester. Where possible, the heat exchanger circulation loop was also sampled on the first day to confirm the results obtained from the digester overflow.
• For the next four weeks, samples were taken daily, and then on alternate days for the following three weeks.
These results gave the washout curve from which can be calculated the actual retention time within the actively mixed zone, the dead volume and the degree of short-circuiting by standard analysis [2,3]. Some of the tracing work performed by the Engineering Contractor did not include this part of the sampling programme.


## 3. NOMINAL AND ACTUAL RETENTION TIMES

The results are given in Figure 2 apart from digesters F and N for which information was not available. The actual retention time is that within the actively mixed zone. In all cases the nominal retention time is greater than the Code of Practice minimum requirement of 12 days for sludges disposed to agricultural land. However, based on actual retention time, four digesters do not meet this requirement. Digester H is just below the guideline value. Fortunately at digester K, the digested sludge is dewatered and then landfilled. For digester T, the lithium tracing exercise was undertaken to assess the hydraulic performance of the digesters at this works prior to major refurbishment; this is now complete. Digester O has had disappointing results in all of the areas under consideration and it was retraced, these results broadly confirmed the first set of results.


## 4. EFECTIVE VOLUME

Figure 3 gives the effective volume for each digester and the time elapsed since it was last empty. The majority of digesters which were originally designed with unconfined gas mixing have an effective volume greater than 80%, the exception being digester K. Also most of the digesters which have been refurbished with unconfined gas mixing have an effective volume greater than 80%, apart from digester O. All of digesters, apart from digester H and O, were designed with facilities to degrit the digester which are used on a fairly regular basis. Since commissioning, digester H has had a rudimentary flushing system installed to degrit the digester but this is thought to be barely adequate. Few of these digesters have been emptied since commissioning. The exception is digester E, which has recently been refurbished and modified from sequential unconfined gas mixing to a continuous system; when emptied the volume of rags and grit was below 10%. Digester K's effective volume is low at 40% and is probably a function of its time in service and the nature of the trade wastes discharged to the works. Digester O has a low aspect ratio with no degritting facilities and these factors have probably contributed to the low effective volume of 64%.

For digesters with Heatamix units, the effective volume is at 90% after 2 years in operation for digester Q. However, for digesters R and S after 10 years in operation the effective volume has fallen to below 50%. There is some actual evidence for this as when digester R was last emptied at least a third of the digester volume consisted of a thick, gritty sludge containing excessive screening.

Digester T, provided with the 'bubble-gun' device has an effective volume of 55%. This has been confirmed to be a reasonable value as when the digesters were cleaned in the past, a significant of debris has been found in them, usually over a third of the volume.

Finally, at digester U, the effective volume is 86% which was considered reasonable for a digester that has not been emptied for the last 10 years. When it was last cleaned, some debris was found.

This 80% effective volume has been acknowledged by increasing the volumes provided on new or refurbished digester schemes that form part of the Company's capital programme.


## 5. MIXING TIME

Results of the mixing times are given in Figure 4. Apart from digesters J and O, the mixing times are below 60 minutes. Digester J is the one provided with sequential unconfined gas mixing and this may be a contributing to the excessive mixing times.


## 6. SHORT CIRCUITNG

The majority of the digesters traced had minimal or no short-circuiting. When investigating the detailed design and operation of the digesters, it was noticeable that there were some common features for the sites that showed minimal short-circuiting. For the newer digesters, the raw sludge is often preheated and the inlet and outlet arrangements are on the opposite sides of the digester. The feeding regimes were also of short duration and usually less than the mixing times within the digester. For some of the older digesters, the sludge is not always preheated but the cold feed sludge is fed into the digester on the opposite side to the digester overflow or as for digester U, where the cold sludge is discharged close to the 'Burper Gun'.

The digesters which showed short-circuiting are given in Table 2.

## Table 2  Short-circuiting results

| Digester | Short - circuiting (%) |
|----------|------------------------|
| G | 6 |
| H | 19 |
| K | 37 |
| O | 31.5 |
| T | 9 |

Both digesters G and H preheat feed sludge, but the inlet and outlet arrangements are only separated by 90° in plan and are at the same level, which has probably given rise to the short-circuiting observed. The short-circuiting in digester K is probably caused by the operational regime of not mixing during charging of the digester with gas mixing commencing when charging stops. Although digester T has a short mixing time, it has a low effective volume, consequently the digester contents are not being mixed adequately. Hence with no preheat of the feed sludge, the cold sludge with a higher density falls to the bottom of the digester where the sludge draw-off pipework is situated and discharges over the overflow.

Digester O, already known to suffer with a low effective volume, also feeds cold sludge directly into the digester. Another factor is the feeding arrangement - the automatic feed control system is unreliable and this results in the feeding of the digesters for extended periods of several hours and with the long mixing time of ninety minutes, raw sludge is not being adequately mixed in.

Finally, digester J with the sequential mixing system, although showing minimal short-circuiting from the mathematical analysis of the washout curve data, gave an indication of short-circuiting on the response graph for the mixing test  (Figure 5). This is probably due to the particular diffuser in  operation at the time of the test.


## 7. CONCLUSIONS

1.  The Company's anaerobic digesters vary widely in their hydraulic performance.

2.  Digesters with unconfined gas mixing generally have an effective volume greater than 80%.

3.  Digesters provided with other mixing systems have a poorer effective volume after prolonged periods of operation. Heatamix units can be expected to have an effective volume of around 50% after ten years in service.

4.  The Company's decision to use continuous unconfined gas mixing in recent years has been validated.

5.  Short-circuiting is not a major problem and when it occurs it can be attributed to one or more of the following:
- poor pipework arrangements
- lack of feed sludge preheat
- poor feeding regimes

6. Mixing is generally effective. The time to homogeneous contents is usually less than 60 minutes.

7. To ensure that guideline treatment conditions are achieved the in digesters, the following are required:
   • pipework arranged so as to minimise short-circuiting
• preheating of the feed sludge
• avoidance of excessive feeding times
• provision of grit withdrawal facilities
• mixing of the digester during the feeding regime
• avoidance of rotary valve systems for unconfined gas mixing as they lead to unacceptable mixing times and may contribute to short-circuiting

## REFERENCES

(1) Rundle, H. and Whyley, J. A Comparison of Gas Recirculation Systems for Mixing the Contents of Digesters. *Wat. Pollut. Control*, 1981 463-480.

(2) Monteith, H.D. and Stephenson , J.P. Mixing Efficiencies in Full-scale Anaerobic Digesters by Tracer Methods. *J Wat. Pollut. Control Fed.*, 1981, 78-84.

(3) Levenspiel, O. *Chemical Reaction Engineering*. John Wiley and Sons, New York,1972

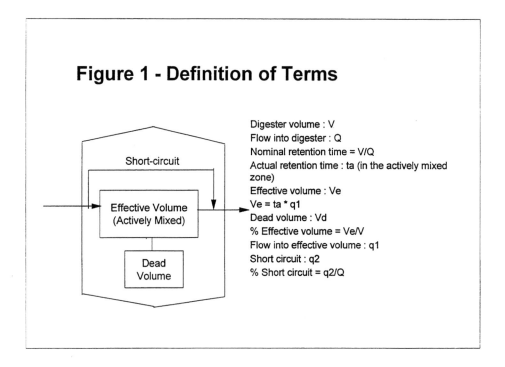

# Figure 1 - Definition of Terms

Digester volume : V
Flow into digester : Q
Nominal retention time = V/Q
Actual retention time : ta (in the actively mixed zone)
Effective volume : Ve
Ve = ta * q1
Dead volume : Vd
% Effective volume = Ve/V
Flow into effective volume : q1
Short circuit : q2
% Short circuit = q2/Q

Short-circuit

Effective Volume (Actively Mixed)

Dead Volume

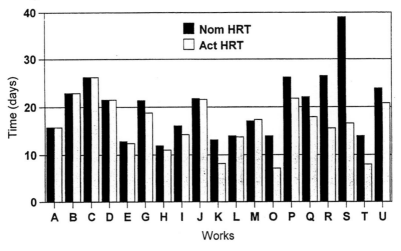

Figure 2 - Nominal & Actual Retention Times

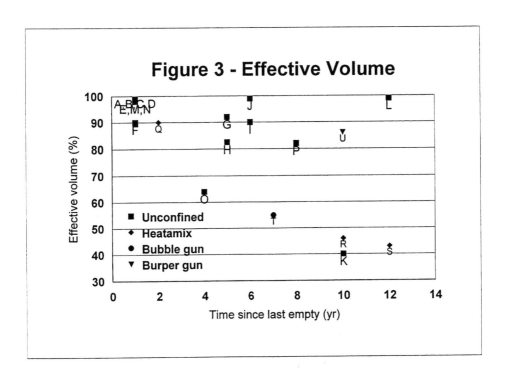

Figure 3 - Effective Volume

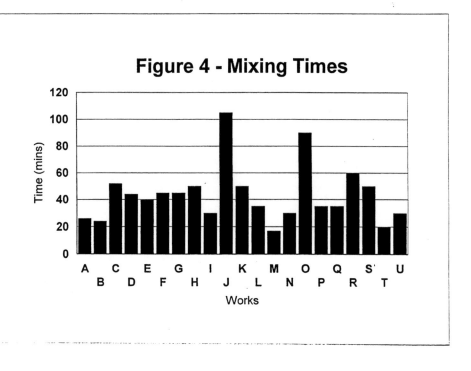

Figure 4 - Mixing Times

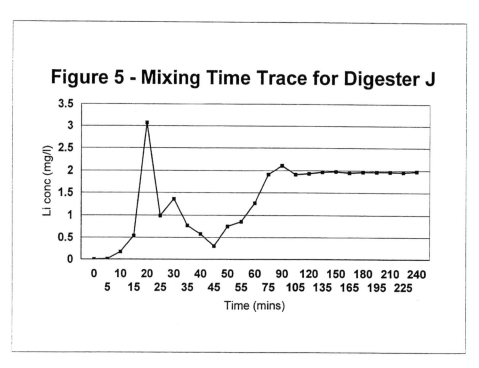

Figure 5 - Mixing Time Trace for Digester J

# Renewal of Mogden STW digester heating and mixing systems

*P May*
*Senior Engineer, Paterson Candy Ltd*

**Synopsis**

Mogden Sewage Treatment works is the second largest in Thames Water, treating a population equivalent of 1.8 Million. During 1998 Thames Water identified that the existing digester heating system was unable to maintain digester temperatures during cold periods and that the mixing systems were suffering repeated failures. The Mogden Project Team commenced work on refurbishing 16 of the 20 digesters in 1999 and are scheduled to complete the work in mid 2002. The paper details the problems encountered with the existing plant, outlines the design constraints affecting both heating and mixing systems and presents the design solutions. Reference is also made to a new digester reseeding method developed to minimise time spent to bring refurbished digesters back into operation.

## 1. INTRODUCTION

Mogden Sewage Treatment Works (STW) is the second largest in Thames Water. The works was constructed in the mid 1930's and subsequently expanded in stages during the 1950's, 1960's and 1990's. The works has a design flow of 800 Ml/d and a maximum flow to treatment of 1600 Ml/d. The existing digestion plant comprises 20 floating roof digesters which are mixed by recirculation of biogas through draft tubes located within the digesters. These units also incorporate hot water jackets for heating the digester contents.

In recent years the performance of the digestion system has deteriorated. The heat recovery from the power house has reduced and the heat exchangers located inside the digesters have not been able to transfer the energy available in the digester heating circuit to maintain digester temperatures in cold periods. Three of the digester roofs were in a poor state and the gas compressors used for the mixing system were suffering frequent failures. Thames Water initiated the project to refurbish the digesters and associated plant as the first phase of sludge stream improvements at the site in 1999. The Mogden Project Team – an alliance between Paterson Candy, Binnie Black and Veatch and Thames Water are currently working to implement the following improvements to the digester plant:

- Temporary digester heating plant
- Permanent 3 MW in-line heating facility for the digester feed line

- Refurbishment of 16 of the 20 digesters including
  - Installation of new heating systems rated to maintain digester temperatures at 35 $^0$C +/- 3 $^0$C
  - Installation of new mixing systems
  - Installing new gas offtake pipework
- Replacement of the floating roofs on 3 digesters
- Modifications to the power station Combined Heat and Power system heat recovery plant
- Installation of a new digester control system

This paper outlines the design solutions selected to meet the above requirements and details how the Mogden Project Team addressed the challenges faced by the requirement to refurbish the digesters within a tight programme on an operational site.


## 2.    OVERVIEW OF EXISTING DIGESTER HEATING SYSTEM

The heat required for the digesters is recovered from Mirrlees Blackstone medium speed dual fuel engines that are located in the works power house. Each engine is fitted with a waste heat boiler for recovering high grade energy from the exhaust gases and separate circuits to recover lower grade heat from the engine jacket water, valve cage and turbocharger intercooler.

Energy is transferred from the digester hot water circuit to the digesters via Simon Hartley Heatamix units. The majority of the digesters have four Heatamix units whilst one digester has five. The Heatamix units consist of a vertical tube through which biogas circulates thereby transferring sludge from low to high level within the digester. A water jacket around the tube transfers energy to the sludge.


## 3.    PROBLEMS WITH THE EXISTING DIGESTER HEATING SYSTEM

Over recent years Thames Water operations staff have found it progressively harder to maintain digester temperatures during anything other than summer months. Tests carried out on the system showed that the digesters were able to absorb 2.5 MW. It was not possible to transfer higher amounts of energy to the digesters as higher feed temperatures merely led to higher return temperatures from the digesters which caused the dual fuel engine water circuits to heat up and led to engine cooling circuit overtemperature trips. These tests identified the digester heat exchangers within the digesters as the limiting factor on energy transfer.

The hot water circuit suffered from loss of water. As no leaks were identified on the pipework to and from the digesters leakage was therefore occurring in the pipework within one or more of the digesters. The makeup water is not softened which has led to scaling problems within pipework and heat exchangers. The system is also fully manually controlled which has led to difficulty in controlling the system.

In addition to the inability to transfer heat to the digesters, the tests on the CHP system showed that the energy recovery was well below the original design criteria. There were also issues with the fundamental design concept of circulating the digester hot water through the engines for jacket water, valve cage and turbocharger intercooling purposes.

## 4.    HEATING SYSTEM DESIGN CONSTRAINTS

The main constraints relating to the heating system were identified as follows:

> The heat exchangers should be rated for the worst case heat demand;
> Heat exchangers should be located external to the digester so that they can be maintained;
> All main sludge and water side components should be safely accessible for operation and maintenance.
> The heat exchangers sludge transfer circuit should be rated for a future 7% DS sludge feed (at present the feed is around 3% DS)`;
> 316L stainless steel sludge pipework, fixtures and fittings within the digester;
> 316L stainless steel heat exchanger material.

## 5.    HEATING SYSTEM DESIGN SOLUTIONS

Digester heat requirement calculations determined that each digester should be fitted with heat exchangers rated at 638kW. This rating represented a worst case heating load for a 5 $^0$C sludge feed; 35 $^0$C required digester temperature; 12 day retention period and $-10$ $^0$C ambient temperature. Whilst this rating would have been reduced if the design criteria had been relaxed, it has led to a couple of benefits. Firstly, the heating system that is capable of rapidly raising digester temperature during commissioning, (when the first two digesters were brought back into service it proved possible to raise the temperature of the final effluent within the digester up to operating temperature within 4 days). Secondly, the system is capable of operation with a degree of tube fouling hindering heat transfer.

The type of heat exchanger was not defined by Thames Water. Shell and tube, spiral tube and external draft tube type arrangements were all considered.

It did not prove possible to fit an external draft tube type heat exchanger in the chambers in between each group of four digesters so this option was rejected. There were differences in opinion as to the benefits and drawbacks of the spiral tube and the shell and tube type heat exchangers and tenders were invited for both systems. The most cost effective system proved to be the shell and tube arrangement. It also proved possible to design a plant layout that fitted within the available space at the mid gallery level whilst meeting requirements for safe access for operation and maintenance.

In order to minimise the possibility of short circuiting the heating loop, the sludge drawoff point was located local to the position of the heat exchanger, but the return location was 135 Degrees around the digester from the drawoff location. The discharge point was also angled to contribute to rotation of the sludge within the digester. Inspection of the digester contents during initial trials of the heating system, without the mixing system operating, showed that the arrangement chosen imparted a rotation to the contents of the digester which in turn would contribute to mixing system performance.

## 6.  HEATING SYSTEM CONTROL

The digester heating system has been integrated with the digester area control system.  All heating system parameters for individual digesters are accessible at the main works control room as well as at the digester area and local to the digester Motor Control Centre.  The control system is set up so that it can be controlled in two different ways:

### 6.1  Digester Temperature Control

Under the Digester Temperature Control mode the operators set a digester temperature setpoint within a presettable range.  At present operators can select any temperature between 33.0 $^0$C and 37.0 $^0$C in 0.1 $^0$C increments.  The range has been set tighter than the +/- 3$^0$C range allowable under the draft regulations to allow for control system overshoot.

Performance of the refurbished digesters shows that the system actually controls the temperature to within +/- 0.5 $^0$C.  The bulk digester temperature drops by approximately 0.5 $^0$C each time the digester is fed with sludge that has not been pre-heated in the in-line heating system.  When the in-line heating system is operating the digester temperature control is approximately +/- 0.2 $^0$C.

### 6.2  Digester Energy Transfer Control

Under the Digester Energy Control mode, the water side of the digester heat exchanger is controlled to maintain a set energy input to the digester.  As more temperature is required to maintain energy transfer the three way valve connected to the hot water circuit is opened, and when less is required the three way valve closes towards recirculation of water within the heat exchanger water side shunt loop.

This mode enables energy input to all digesters to be balanced depending on individual digester operating conditions.  It also limits the amount of energy that any one digester can draw.  This helps maintain stable operation of all operating digesters.

## 7.  TEMPORARY HEATING SYSTEM

Due to the arrangement of sludge feed and draw pipework to the digesters the only practical way of managing the digester refurbishment process was to work on groups of four digesters at a time. This led to concerns from operational staff about the performance of the remaining 16 digesters when the first four digesters were removed from service.  In particular, the digesters remained in service would have approximately 25% increased heating requirement, yet there were known to be severe limitations in the amount of energy that could be transferred from the hot water circuit to the digesters.  The system was also liable to large additional heat demands during periods that refurbished digesters were to be brought on-line.

The solution chosen to address this problem for the first group of four digesters to be refurbished was to hire a temporary heating system that would heat the sludge in the thickened sludge holding tanks prior to it being fed to the digesters.  This system consisted of a packaged boiler plant that raised steam that was injected directly into the thickened sludge holding tanks via lances.

The system worked extremely well in terms of raising the temperature of the raw feed sludge up to around 30 $^0$C but had the side effect of outstripping the ability of the old odour control plant to deal with the odours. The solution to this short term problem was to install a temporary odour control plant to augment the existing system.

The benefit of heating the sludge in the thickened sludge holding tank was that this was a completely separate route to providing the required energy input to the digesters. As heating up the raw sludge to digester operating temperature represents up to three quarters of the total heat demand, the ability to heat the feed sludge significantly reduced the reliance on poorly performing heat exchangers within the digesters.

## 8. PERMANENT IN-LINE HEATING SYSTEM

The calculated worst case heat demand for the digester system exceeded the design values of heat recovery from the power house CHP system. It was therefore decided that a permanent in-line heating facility would be installed. The in-line heating system was rated at 3 MW energy transfer to the feed sludge. This rating was selected on the basis of the shortfall in energy that can be recovered via the CHP system compared to that required by the digesters under the worst case design heating load.
This system offers two particular benefits:

Firstly, in terms of bringing digesters into service following refurbishment, an in-line heating system enables the impact on digesters that are in service to be minimised;

Secondly, the integrity of the digester plant is increased in that two independent means of putting energy into digesters exists.

Both these benefits can be achieved at the same time as increasing the maximum energy that can be transferred to the digesters.

## 9. OVERVIEW OF EXISTING DIGESTER MIXING SYSTEM

The existing digester mixing system for each digester consists of a ground level gas compressor that simultaneously delivers biogas to the base of the multiple Simon Hartley Heatamix units located within the digester. At the base of each Heatamix unit is a toroidal chamber into which the gas is delivered. When the gas has built up to a finite level it "burps" out into the vertical pipe around which the hot water jacket is located and sludge is thereby transferred from the bottom to top of the digester.

## 10. PROBLEMS WITH THE EXISTING DIGESTER MIXING SYSTEM

The existing digester mixing was not performing well. A number of the compressors were suffering repeated failures and at the start of the current project there were fewer compressors than digesters in service.

As stated previously, there was also a failure to transfer the rated amount of energy to the sludge. Tests that had been carried out on a digester that had been cleaned out indicated that the basic system concept was sound, but in practise the performance could drop off rapidly.

Once cleaning started on the first digester the cause of the poor mixing and heat transfer started to become apparent. The heatamix units vertical pipe were, in almost every case, blocked with rags and deposits. The blockages were not visible due to the nature of the heatamix system where all components are submerged within the digester, and likewise there was no means of cleaning out these units other than by emptying out the sludge from within the digester, which incurred considerable cost.

## 11. MIXING SYSTEM DESIGN CONSTRAINTS

The primary constraint on the mixing system was that it needed to meet the following acceptance criteria: 120

Feed sludge dispersal within 60 minutes of its introduction;

Tracer concentration over the period 1 to 4 hours from commencement of the test is within 10 % of the theoretical concentration calculated from the mass of tracer added and the working volume of the digester taking into account background levels;

A minimum of 90% tracer recovery during the mixing test;

No more than 5% of feed volume short circuits the digester;

Dead volume as calculated from the daily feed rate and the residence time calculated from the exponential tracer die-away curve is not greater than 10% of the working volume of the digester.

The mixing system also had to be designed to meet the following criteria:

The mixing system was to be rated for a future 7% DS sludge feed;

Main mixing system components to be located external to the digester;

All components to be safely accessible for operation and maintenance;

Electrical equipment located near the top of the digesters to be zone 1 rated.

## 12. MIXING SYSTEM DESIGN SOLUTIONS

The choice of mixing system raised a considerable amount of debate. Principal options included pumped mixing systems and gas mixing systems. At the initial stages of the contract the potential for installing blade mixing was raised, but rejected owing to the floating dome design of the digester roofs and the digester aspect ratio. External draft tube designs were also rejected due to space constraints within the digester mid level gallery as detailed earlier.

Of the above systems, the main discussions centred on pumped mixing systems and unconfined sequential gas mixing systems. The principal concern relating to the pumped systems was that increasing thickness of feed sludge from the current value of around 3% DS up to the design value of 7% DS would result in significant increases in input power and flow rate to meet the rated mixing performance in comparison to the gas mixing systems. Gas mixing systems were well known to the team and the perception was that there was a reduced risk associated with installation of this system at Mogden.

76

The system was subject to competitive tender and the most cost effective offer was that provided by Monsal Ltd. The Monsal installation utilised lower installed compressor capacity than their competitors. Their design was determined on the basis of research that they had jointly funded with Yorkshire Water and that had been carried out by the BHR group.

## 13.  MIXING SYSTEM CONTROL

The sequential gas mixing system that Monsal offered utilises 9 separate injection points. The gas is directed to one injection point at a time, but incorporates a short duration when two points are open simultaneously to prevent high discharge pressures in the delivery lines from the gas compressor. The system is also controlled to ensure that the nozzle nearest to the digester sludge feed line is used at the start of each digester feed.

The control system also checks which of the discharge solenoid valves are operable and ensures that the system bypasses up to five units failed to maintain mixing system operation.

Control of the digester mixing system is integrated with the digester area control system. Status of the mixing systems, for each digester, together with all appropriate control parameters, are accessible at the works central control room as well as at operator interfaces in the digester area and adjacent to the digester area Motor Control Centre.

## 14.  DIGESTER RESEEDING PROCEDURE

The digester work programme was tight from the start and delays were encountered with initial handover of digesters due to operational constraints and also with the time taken to clean the grit out of the digesters prior to installation of new plant. In order to recover time and meet the project deadlines a new reseeding procedure was developed and implemented.

The standing procedure was to fill a digester that was to be brought on line with final effluent, purge it back into service and then commence heating and slowly raise the sludge feed over the next 30 days.

The team developed a new procedure for reseeding the digeseters whereby approximately 4000 m$^3$ of digested sludge was transferred from operational digesters into the digester to be reseeded over a 3 day period.

To carry out the reseeding, a recirculation line was installed that connected the discharge line from the digested sludge pumps to the delivery line to the digesters. A digester drawdown sequence was run on all operational digesters and the sludge recirculated into the digester to be reseeded. Simultaneously, effluent was withdrawn via the digester gas seal at the same rate as the digested sludge was being fed into the digester. Following one reseeding operation on the first day, the operational digesters were refilled overnight and operated over the next day to reduce sludge that has built up in the works during the reseeding operation. The reseeding operation was then repeated on the third day.

Experience of this process showed that digesters were producing small amounts of gas after the first reseeding operation and over the couple of days following the second feed operation came up to normal levels of gas production in relation to the sludge feed. The feed regime started at 60 % of the rated feed and increased up to full feed within a week.


## 15.    CONCLUSIONS

The team have been successful in delivering a complex job within tight time constraints and under difficult working conditions. There has been particular success in maintaining focus on the safety of the installation for construction, operation and maintenance personnel. The project is currently 60 % complete and is on track to deliver refurbished digesters on programme.

The digester heating systems have been fitted within the mid level galleries without compromising access. The plant operates reliably, achieves fine levels of digester temperature control and is accessible for both operation and maintenance.

The digester mixing systems use approximately one third of the energy of the units that they replace and have performed reliably. Mixing tests are scheduled for July 2001.

In relation to project delivery, the team have taken steps to maintain programme and as a result of developing and implementing a new digester reseeding procedure have saved a considerable amount of time commissioning refurbished digesters.

# SLUDGE MANAGEMENT

# Testing and costing a novel pasteurisation process for the treatment of sewage sludges

*Isabelle Michel*
*Purac Ltd.*

## AKNOWLEDGEMENTS

Purac Ltd. would like to thank Anglian Water Innovation for their involvement and part funding of this project, the staff of Cambridge Sewage Treatment Works for their site support, Anglian Water laboratories, Vivienne Taylor at DERA, Louise Fletcher and Nigel Horan from Leeds University for their work, advice and support.

## ABSTRACT

The revision of the UK code of Practice for Agricultural Use of Sewage sludge has increased the need for advanced sludge treatments. Purac Ltd have designed and tested a full-scale pasteurisation plant operating as a continuous process that incorporates internal batching and heat recovery.

The bacteriological results showed that <u>Escherichia coli</u>, Salmonella and Enteroviruses were reduced to levels barely detectable in the pasteurised sludge and that the log reduction achieved for <u>E.coli</u> was on average 7.6 log. Complementary analyses investigated the soluble BOD, total COD, dry and volatile solids levels of the sludge.

Commercial comparison with drying and lime stabilisation plants showed that the Capex and the Opex of the PUR*iser* plant are very competitive.

## 1. THE NEED FOR ADVANCED SLUDGE TREATMENT

The use of sewage sludge in agriculture has been practised for many years and in many countries. However, recently the British Retail Consortium (BRC) amongst others have expressed concerns over the pathogen levels in the sludge applied to land and recent health scares have raised public awareness.

Within the UK, the DoE Code of Practice (1989) defines the permitted application of sludge to farmland. This is currently in the course of revision (1) and due for re-issue 2001. It presents a set of effective sludge processes that can significantly reduce the pathogen content of the sludge (bacteria, viruses, protozoa and helminths), which represent a health hazard for man. In order to address the concerns of the BRC amongst others, the UK water industry has adopted the "Safe Sludge Matrix" (2), which further regulates the use of sludge in agriculture.

This has meant that there is an increased need for "advanced" treatment of sewage sludge, such as thermal drying, composting and pasteurisation. More recently the European Commission has issued a draft Sludge Directive (3), which would indicate a movement toward a three categories of sludge approach, quite similar to the US EPA standards. "Advanced treated" sludges are envisaged as being intended for domestic and agricultural use with "conventionally treated" sludges for restricted farm use. Untreated sludges will not be used.

## 2. DESIGNING A NEW PASTEURISATION PLANT

### 2.1. Design philosophy
In order to meet perceived industry needs, the vast majority of the future pasteurisation plants will likely be retrofitted into existing works. Therefore future pasteurisation plant should incorporate the following features:
> Be a "bolt-on" pasteurisation plant
> Utilisation of the existing assets (predominantly heat raising plant is by dual fuel hot water boilers)
> Minimisation of the need for additional heating plant and operational costs
> Small footprint
> Operator-friendly
> Be as un-disruptive to current operations as possible both in terms of installation / commissioning and future operation.

For the reasons outlined above Alfa Laval spiral heat exchangers incorporating heat recovery were chosen, in particular for their compactness and their ease of cleaning, and the design of the PUR*iser* was jointly developed by Purac and Alfa Laval. The plant has a small footprint and utilises well proven components.

### 2.2 Design basis and description of the PUR*iser*

#### 2.2.1. Design basis
The unit under trial was a full-scale plant. It is now installed at Lowestoft STW, which is currently under construction. It treats a raw sludge with maximum percentage dry solids of 8%; the maximum flow through the unit is 17 m³/hr (13.8 m³/hr on average). The unit uses four spiral heat exchangers: a sludge/sludge heat exchanger through which the heat is recovered, two hot water exchangers and one cooler.

The current perception of pasteurisation in the industry is that the only acceptable system is a batch process. Intermittent running however is not ideal for operation of the heat exchangers. In order to optimise heat recovery, a continuous feed and discharge pasteurisation process that incorporates internal batching has therefore been developed and built. This configuration offers a number of advantages: maintaining steady state conditions both up and downstream, reducing the mechanical complexity, and reducing capital cost. Pasteurisation will be at not less than 70°C for a minimum of 30 minutes as specified in the current Code of Practice. Heating will be by means of sludge-sludge heat recovery, followed by hot water at 90°C, both duties taking place in spiral exchangers (see figure 9).

The pasteurisation plant is designed to replace the conventional external heating circuit on a mesophilic or thermophilic digestion plant. The heat exchange will be controlled to ensure that pasteurised sludge will be discharged at the temperature required by the downstream digestion process.

The design results in low odour emission from the pasteurisation tank by containing the odour inside the unit. Head space exchange inside the unit means that there is no net egress of odorous air once the plant is up and running.

### 2.2.2. *Fouling of the heat exchangers*
Fouling of heat exchange elements on the sludge side in hot water (at greater than conventional temperatures) is commonly perceived to be due to sludge "baking". The term Baking here refers to protein and other compounds breaking down on the surface of the exchangers leaving a resistant residue that reduces the heat transfer ability of the unit. This phenomenon has been regarded by the water industry historically to occur when operating sludge heat exchangers at water temperatures higher than 60 to 70°C. In the PUR*iser* this has been alleviated by using an internal recycle. It allows the sludge throughput to be reduced whilst still maintaining high velocities and good heat transfer coefficients. Other comparable systems tend to be fixed speed devices necessitating idle time at less than design duties. As heat exchangers operate best continually reject product is the unavoidable result. The high degree of turndown achievable by the PUR*iser* enables continuous operation of the pasteurisation unit from the point of commissioning, potentially years before the design horizon thereby enabling continuous Digester feed and optimal Heat exchange operation at all times.

### 2.2.3. *Quality control*
In order to ensure that a batch is pasteurised, its retention time is recorded and the temperature of the batch is measured as the batch exits the unit. If any of the two parameters does not comply with the process requirements of 30 minutes and 70°C, the failed batch is discarded and the following passed batch is used to flush the pipework clear. Both batches are then re-processed. A log of every batch is kept detailing the conditions the sludge experienced and stored for QA purposes.


## 3. TESTING THE PURISER AT CAMBRIDGE STW

### 3.1. Set up of Cambridge STW Trials
The pasteurisation plant was installed between the thickening and the mesophilic digestion stages of the sludge treatment works. The sludge treated at Cambridge is a blend of co-settled sludge (humus and primary sludge), SAS and imported sludge and has a heavy rag loading. Before pasteurisation, the sludge was screened to 5mm.

On average, the sludge throughput at Cambridge STW is 500 m$^3$/day (21 m$^3$/hr). A portion of this flow was passed forward to the pasteurisation plant.

### 3.2. Performance of the pasteurisation unit

#### 3.2.1. *Pathogens reduction*

3.2.1.1. *Salmonella*
The raw sludge contained between 31 and 9100 counts per 10g of wet sludge (140 to 41930 counts per g of dry sludge). Early samples were recorded simply as above 1,800 counts per 10g of wet sludge (figure 1). The results show that the pasteurised sludge contained consistently less than 10 bacteria per 10g of wet sludge. This corresponds to a reduction of 1.9Log on average. The maximum log reduction achieved was 3Log.

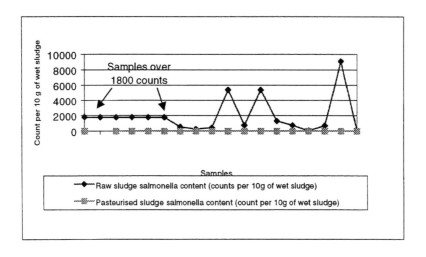

**Figure 1: Salmonella content in raw and pasteurised sludge**

3.2.1.2. *Escherichia coli*
The results for E.coli are also encouraging. The arithmetic average content of the raw sludge is $6.15 \ E10^6$ counts per 10 g of wet sludge (or $3.1E10^7$ count per g of dry sludge, see figure 2). Again, early analyses did not detail the counts less than 2000 counts of E.coli. The precision was later improved to 20 counts per 10g of wet sludge toward the end of the trials. The analyses were carried out by Anglian Water and further analytical work to more accurately evaluate the log kill achieved was carried out by DERA Porton (Defence Evaluation and Research Association). During the trials, an independent body through the University of Leeds funded by the DETR carried out analyses as part of a wider study aimed at establishing current practice and the efficacy of other more advanced sludge processes on pathogen removal.

## Table 1: E.coli measurements from Leeds University and DERA

| Raw sludge concentration (counts per g of dry sludge) | Pasteurised sludge concentration (counts per g of dry sludge) | Log kill |
|---|---|---|
| $1.4\,E10^7$ | Not detected | 7.1 |
| $7.4\,E10^6$ | Not detected | 6.9 |
| $5.9E10^7$ | Not detected | 7.8 |
| $2.5\,E10^8$ | Not detected | 8.4 |
| $1.7\,E10^8$ | Not detected | 8.2 |
| $7.4\,E10^8$ | Not detected | 8.9 |
| $1.4\,E10^7$ | Not detected | 7.1 |
| $3.5\,E10^6$ | Not detected | 6.5 |
| $5.1\,E10^7$ | Not detected | 7.7 |

Despite the low resolution of early analyses, later analysis demonstrates that the process can kill off <u>E.coli</u> to levels that are barely detectable. Some pasteurised sludge samples however showed measurable levels of E.coli (up to $4\,E10^4$ counts). These were invariably from the first sample taken in the day and it is suggested that insufficient flushing of the pipe was carried out prior to sampling, thereby allowing for re-contamination of the sample. This was not observed for the samples analysed for salmonella.

The results from DERA laboratory and Leeds University show that providing there are sufficient E.coli in the raw sludge, the log reduction can be in excess of log 6. On average 7.6 Log reduction is readily achievable up to a maximum of 8.9 log.

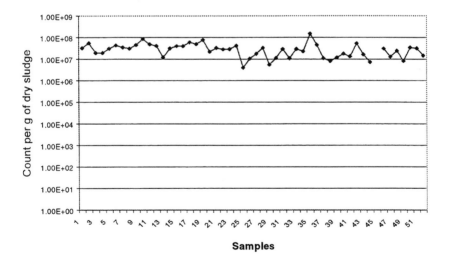

Figure 2: Raw sludge content in E.coli

### 3.2.1.3. Enteroviruses

Enteroviruses analysis was additionally undertaken by the University of Leeds. Unconfirmed indications would show that the enteroviruses are absent from pasteurised sludge.

### 3.2.2. Complementary analyses

#### 3.2.2.1. Percentage Volatile Solids

The sludge at Cambridge has a maximum thickness of 4%DS and this therefore did not allow the pasteurisation plant to be tested at its design thickness specification.

The percentage Volatile Solids of the sludge was measured daily.

Although no change in Dry Solids content was observed through pasteurisation, there would appear to be a slight increase in Volatile Solids (2% increase on average).

#### 3.2.2.2. COD and soluble BOD

The results are presented in figures 3 and 4. An increase can be noticed in the soluble BOD after pasteurisation. On average, the sBOD in the raw sludge is 1006 mg/l and 1444 mg/l in the pasteurised sludge. The arithmetic average increase in soluble BOD is 30%, but on some occasions there was no increase at all. There is too little data to make statistical analysis of this set of results, though the trend suggests that there is an increase in soluble BOD.

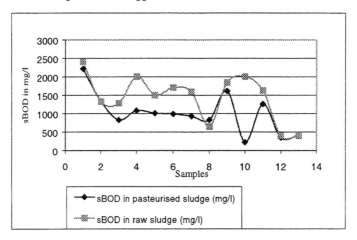

**Figure 3: soluble BOD concentrations in raw and pasteurised sludge**

In the heating process cellular material is broken down and organic components in the sludge are released into the surrounding liquor. The 30% average increase in sBOD that was observed in the pasteurised sludge demonstrates this. Hence as more easily digestible compounds are available to the anaerobic biomass greater levels of stabilisation should be achieved. Literature suggests that a 50% destruction in Volatile Solids can be readily achieved after pasteurisation, compared to the more usual 40 to 45% typical in conventional digestion.

The influence of pasteurisation on the Total COD is less obvious. On average, the raw sludge content is 23,550 mg/l and the pasteurised sludge content 26,000 mg/l. This would suggest an increase of Total COD during pasteurisation.

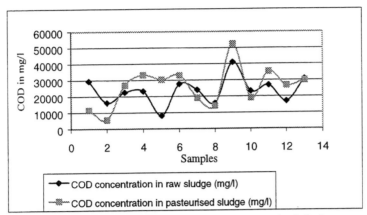

**Figure 4: COD concentration in raw and pasteurised sludge**

But no change in Total COD concentration was expected after pasteurisation and this was confirmed by the trends. There seems to be a wide variation of the Total COD between the raw and the pasteurised sludge. This may be due to the fact that the samples may not correspond to a same batch. However the variation is greater than what could be expected as every batch is subjected to the same conditions and more likely because the incoming sludge characteristics vary considerably and the CODs are likely to vary correspondingly.

The set up of the trials did not allow us to assess likely improvement in the digesters operation at Cambridge. The unit was pasteurising only a part of the sludge flow and no measurement of the gas production was available on site.

*3.2.2.3. Tracer tests*
Lithium Chloride was injected in the process and measured at the outlet of the plant at discrete time intervals to determine the nature of the batch process. Tests were carried out at the beginning and at the end of the trials using washwater and sludge.

The tracer analysis demonstrates that the hydraulic retention time of the sludge is at least 30 minutes within the pasteurisation unit. No Lithium was detected in the outlet stream until 80 minutes after injection in the inlet stream at the maximum design feed rate (see figure 5). We can therefore conclude that there is no short-circuiting of the sludge path inside the tank and that there is no leakage in between the internal sections of the unit.

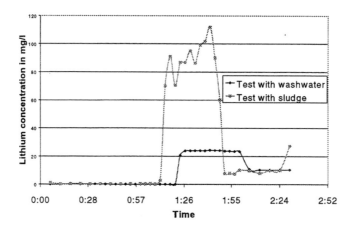

**Figure 5: Tracer tests with Lithium Chloride using sludge and washwater**

*3.2.2.4. Odour measurements*
The sample point in the vent before the odour abatement unit exhibits measurable levels of $H_2S$. Measurements show that during continuous operation of the plant, the content of $H_2S$ in the vent stream was 1 ppm on average (Draeger tubes), reaching a maximum of 7 ppm on one occasion. The inside of the pasteurisation unit was also inspected while containing hot sludge and $H_2S$ measurements were taken. These indicated that more than 500ppm of $H_2S$ (off scale) were contained in the headspace of the unit i.e. high levels.

Draeger tube analysis did not detect any concentrations of ammonia and the Crowcon monitor consistently indicated that the air stream was free of methane.

The outlet air from the odour treatment unit contained no measurable levels of any of the above.

The findings show that the pasteurisation process generates little additional odour. This will obviously depend on the sludge type and characteristics and may differ from one site to another. As intended at the design phase, the odour is displaced internally as levels of $H_2S$ emitted from the odour duct were significantly lower during operation than those witnessed within the tank.

**3.2.3. Heat exchangers performance**

*3.2.3.1. Overall Heat Transfer coefficient and pressure drop*
The pressure drop and the Overall Heat Transfer Coefficient (OHTC) in each heat exchanger were measured for various sludge flows. Measurements were taken continuously throughout the day and then averaged over 24 hours. The results for the heat recovery heat exchanger and the first hot water heat exchanger are presented in the tables below.

**Table 2: Heat recovery heat exchanger performance**

| Feed flow (m³/hr) | P drop on cold side (bar) | P drop on hot side (bar) | OHTC (W/m².°K) |
|---|---|---|---|
| 16.7 | 1.13 | 1.6 | 1425.4 |
| 16.5 | 1.19 | 1.66 | 1543.6 |
| 14.5 | 0.79 | 1.21 | 1244.8 |
| 13.3 | 0.82 | 1.46 | 1045.0 |
| 11.2 | 0.69 | 1.16 | 809.4 |
| 7.9 | 0.36 | 0.75 | 576.8 |
| **Design** 17 | **4.19** | **2.98** | **489.8** |

The difference in the pressure drop between the trials and the design values are explained by the difference in sludge thickness.

The heat recovery heat exchanger can achieve a maximum OHTC of 1544 $W/m^2$.deg K, which is more than its design OHT coefficient of 490 $W/m^2$.K at 17 $m^3$/hr. The explanation to this wide difference is again due to the sludge characteristics. As the dry solids content of the Cambridge Sludge is less than the design 8%DS, the sludge was less viscous and the fluid film adjacent to the heat exchanger wall therefore thinner (4), hence increasing the amount of heat exchange between the two fluids. Comparison with Design data for a 4% sludge has not been made to date.

The sludge after heat recovery reached a maximum of 55.5°C (on average 31.4°C was the recovered outlet temperature instead of 21.3°C as quoted in the design). This temperature value was maintained throughout the trials independently of the sludge flow. The OHT coefficient decreases with the sludge flow as the fluid film gets thicker (See table 3). The lowest OHT rate reached was 580$W/m^2$.K for the minimum design flow 8$m^3$/h, which is still higher than the design specification. Whilst there cannot be a problem of baking in the heat recovery exchanger there is however still the risk of fouling and the performance would likely decrease after operation without a Cleaning In Place (CIP) system or planned routine maintenance.

**Table 3: Hot water heat exchanger performance**

| Feed flow (m³/hr) | Recirculation flow (m³/hr) | Pressure drop (bar) | Hot water flow (m³/hr) | OHTC (W/m².°K) |
|---|---|---|---|---|
| 16.7 | 15.6 | 1.86 | 4.3 | 809.4 |
| 14.5 | 16.8 | 1.62 | 5.36 | 639.1 |
| 16.5 | 6.2 | 1.16 | 5.41 | 1029.5 |
| 11.2 | 6.3 | 0.75 | 3.31 | 639.0 |
| 13.3 | 0.6 | 0.55 | 4.41 | 870.0 |
| 7.9 | 0.6 | 0.26 | 4.38 | 863.2 |
| **Design** 17 | **0** | **2.53** | **15** | **807.6** |

The OHT of the hot water heat exchangers varies from one testing period to the next. On average, the heat transfer is 808.4$W/m^2$.°K, very similar to the one quoted in the design (807.6 $W/m^2$.K). However, the OHTC values have varied widely (from 640 up to 1100 $W/m^2$.K).

Because the sludge is thinner, the OHTC would have been expected to be higher than the design value. However, the relationship between Heat Transfer coefficients and the flow and temperature of hot water is extremely sensitive (see formula below). The OHTC decreases with the hot water flow as would be expected (thicker fluid film layer on the water side). During the trials, the hot water flow required was less than in the design: on average 4.5 $m^3$/hr instead of 15$m^3$/hr and the temperature increase across the hot water heat exchanger was less: 5.7°C instead of 22°C. This can be attributed to the efficient heat recovery of the sludge / sludge heat exchanger as explained above. Furthermore, some difficulties in maintaining a constant hot water flow for a given sludge flow were experienced and therefore the OHT coefficient varied.

The OHTC values were evaluated using the following formula:

$$Q \ (kW) = OHTC \ (W/m^2.K) \ x \ Surface \ Area \ (m^2) \ x \ LMTD$$

LMTD is the Logarithmic Mean Temperature Difference in degree K.

$$LMTD = ((T_1\text{-}t_2)\text{-}(T_2\text{-}t_1)) \ / \ ln((T_1\text{-}t_2)/(T_2\text{-}t_1))$$

$T_1$ and $T_2$= inlet and outlet temperature of hot fluid
$t_1$ and $t_2$ = inlet and outlet temperature of cold fluid

It had been expected that by monitoring OHTC the degree of baking could be predicted and used for diagnostic purposes. The baking, however, was so minimal during the trials that this was not practicable.

### 3.2.3.2. Fouling in the hot water heat exchangers

There is no apparent trend between the sludge velocity (or sludge througput) in the hot water heat exchangers and the OHT (table 3), therefore it is not possible to draw any conclusion regarding baking in the heat exchangers.

The trials were completed by a visual inspection of the heat exchangers internal channel.

The two hot water heat exchangers showed no trace of baking after two and a half month of operation. Their internal channels were completely clean with no trace of deposit or pertinacious film.
The heat recovery heat exchanger had a slight film on the cold side, but was free of gross deposits. On the hot side of the heat recovery heat exchanger, a light deposit of fat was observed.
Inspection of the cooler showed that the layer of fat was thicker (0.5 mm) and had coated the channels. The pipework between the heat recovery heat exchanger and the cooler was also coated with a thin layer of fat, as for the inside of the pipe between the two heat exchangers, corroborating the observation that fat appears to deposit on the cooling faces of the heat exchangers.

None of these deposits had affected the PUR*iser* performance.

# 4. COMMERCIALISING THE PUR*iser*

## 4.1. Improving the design and costing the unit

### 4.1.1. Design review
Overall, the plant has been successfully commissioned at Cambridge: pasteurised batches were continuously passed forward to the digesters and sludge baking was efficiently controlled. Yet the trials gave Purac an opportunity to further improve the plant design. For instance:
- An easy retrofit option for a mixing device has been installed
- The number of temperature transmitters has been optimised
- An intermittent hot water recycling loop has been installed around the cooling surfaces of the heat exchangers to control fat deposition.

### 4.1.2. A costing model for the PURiser
Purac have tried to put together a simple way of costing the PUR*iser* plant, based on the estimated plant yearly sludge throughput and the percentage dry solids of the sludge. Twelve design cases were studied: 4,000, 6,000 and 8,000 tonnes dry solids per annum at 5%, 6%, 7% and 8%DS sludge.

For commercial reasons, details of the complete model cannot be provided, but figures 7 and 8 indicate capital costs and operational costs per tonne of dry solids treated over a year. The cost for each case is only an estimate, since the design must also take into account the sludge percentage dry solids, the sludge volumetric throughput ($m^3$/day) and the configuration of the existing digesters.

The capital costs do not include for the civil costs, which are site dependant. The pasteurisation plant requires a concrete slab (typically 10 meters by 17 meters) and trenches for the new pipelines.

## 4.2. Approaching the sludge treatment market

### 4.2.1. Arguments in favour of the PURiser
Proposed European legislation strongly leads the way toward more stringent sludge standards on pathogens, metals and organic compounds. Unfortunately, tight consents, particularly on metals, tend to drive away the decision-makers from the option of recycling some sludges to land. Since landfill long-term route is now virtually closed for sludge disposal, destructive technologies could seem an attractive solution. However, the new climate levy and the new European Incineration Directive also impose restrictions on incineration plants, in particular on the $CO_2$ emission levels. On the other hand, gasification is an innovative solution, which is able to produce "green energy" and will qualify for exemption from the climate levy, but it is still at its early development stage in Europe. There is therefore a real need to find a means of meeting the interim requirements for control of pathogens in sludges recycled to agriculture.

The main argument for the pasteurisation process is its environmentally friendly character. Recycling the sludge and the nutrients it contains to land has been practised for years. Choosing pasteurisation allows using established routes for sludge re-use while addressing the general public concerns. It is the best and quickest option for the Water Companies that rely on their relation with farmers. Furthermore, thermal pasteurisation produces a minimal amount of odour, does not use chemicals and requires a few simple civil structures. There are also other advantages, which need to be scientifically quantified, for instance the increase in gas production.

But the most convincing argument relates to the economics of the pasteurisation plant. The decision of implementing thermal treatment of sludge is in the hands of plant operators and managers, whose main concern is the impact of the new plant on their annual budget.

### 4.2.1.1. Heating costs

The heating costs are usually not considered in the operational costs because the energy for heating is provided by the plant itself (the biogas produced in the digestion plant is used in dual-fuel boilers). However, reassurance needs to be given that the biogas consumption will not exceed the digestion plant gas production and that additional fuel will not be used.

The main feature of the PUR*iser* is to incorporate heat recovery and to make the existing sludge recirculation system around the digesters redundant. The pasteurised sludge is fed at the temperature needed for mesophilic (or thermophilic) digestion and compensates the heat losses in the system and in the digesters.

Figure 6 shows the typical temperature profiles across a sludge digestion plant and across a sludge plant incorporating the PUR*iser* prior to digestion. All the figures quoted below are rough estimates.

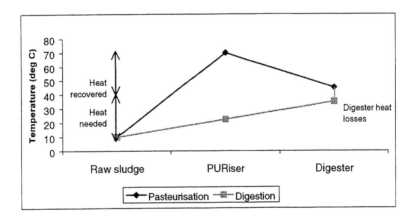

**Figure 6: Typical temperature profiles: pre-pasteurisation vs. digestion**

In order to heat the sludge from 10°C up to 70°C, the PUR*iser* needs a heat input of 35°C if it recovers 25°C for instance. This is the same for the digestion plant, which raises the sludge temperature from 10°C up to 35°C, but must also compensate for the digester heat losses by heating up the sludge to an additional 10°C. The heat input is therefore the same for the PUR*iser* system and the digestion plant. Heat losses in the additional pipework for the pasteurisation plant are considered negligible (it is lagged).

However, the PUR*iser* system is designed for several situations taking into account the variations of the sludge throughput and of the seasonal temperatures. It is possible that for some sludge plants in summer time, the capacity of the heat recovery heat exchanger will become overloaded. A cooler may be necessary to further decrease the temperature of the sludge. In this case, a part of the heat is not recovered.

But the heat input to the PUR*iser* is still the same as when the cooler is not used. The amount of heat recovered could have been higher and is only limited by the heat recovery heat exchanger size. In this case, there will be more gas consumption with pre-pasteurisation than with digestion only, but the increase in gas consumption will not exceed the plant gas production. We have indeed showed that when the cooler is not used, the heat input to pasteurisation plant is the same as for the digestion plant. Additionally, the gas production is likely to increase after retrofit of the pre-pasteurisation unit.

*4.2.1.2. Pumping costs*
The table below gives the details of the pumps used in a digestion plant and in a pre-pasteurisation plant.

**Table 4: Pumps in digestion and PUR*iser* plants.**

| Pumps type | Digestion | Pre-Pasteurisation |
|---|---|---|
| Digesters Recirculation pumps | One set (PC) | Disused |
| Hot water pumps | One set | Replaced by smaller pumps (centrifugal) |
| Washwater pumps | Not used | Tapping into the existing washwater system, no need for new pumps. |
| Feed pumps | One set (PC) | Re-use existing pumps or new pumps (PC) |
| Pasteurisation recirculation pumps | No | One new set (PC) |
| Pasteurised sludge pumps | No | One new set (PC) |

Based on the absorbed power of the progressive cavity pumps and a value of 4.5p/kW for the electricity costs, the power consumption of the PUR*iser* have been calculated for 12 design cases using the following formula for each set of pumps:

*Power consumption (£/year) = Power absorbed (kW) × 0.75× 24 × 365 × 4.5 p/kW*

*(with 0.75 = ratio average/maximum power consumption)*

The range of power consumption falls between £1,900 and £4,000. However, this does not take into account the fact that the existing digester recirculation pumps and the existing hot water pumps will be disused. The additional power consumption will therefore be lower than the values quoted above.

*4.2.2. Pasteurisation techniques*
In Europe, pasteurisation of sewage sludge has been used for the last 20 years and the market is already established, especially in Germany and Switzerland.

## Table 5: Pre-pasteurisation processes

| Type of heating | Advantages | Disadvantages |
|---|---|---|
| *High temperature/ pressure system (thermal hydrolysis)* | • The reduction of dry solids in digestion is higher than for the other pre-pasteurisation processes<br>• Biogas production likely to increase further | • High operating costs<br>• Use of high pressure and steam injection technology |
| *Direct heating by steam injection* | • No risk of sludge baking in heat exchangers | • Increase the sludge volume by up to10%<br>• If retrofitted to an existing plant, need of new steam boilers |
| *Direct heating by submerged combustion* | • No risk of sludge baking in heat exchangers<br>• Very efficient heat transfer<br>• Easy retrofit to existing installation | • Not common in the water industry<br>• Usually do not incorporate heat recovery (but not always)<br>• High odour levels |
| *Indirect heating (heat exchange)* | • Use of existing boilers<br>• Familiar technology to plant operators | • Risk of sludge baking in the hot water heat exchangers |
| *Heat of reaction processes (aerobic oxidation)* | • Heat is generated by the process | • Complementary heating is still needed<br>• Higher operating costs (air blowers)<br>• Higher odour levels |
| **Other options** | **Advantages** | **Disadvantages** |
| *Continuous process* | • One tank system | • Risk of process short-circuiting |
| *Batch process* | • A minimum retention time is guaranteed<br>• Easy quality audit | • Three tanks are necessary |
| *No heat recovery* | • No dependency on sludge load to recover energy | • Increase of the operational costs<br>• Biogas production may not be sufficient<br>• Increase of Capex if additional boilers are needed. |

The PUR*iser* is a batch system with indirect heating and has addressed the risk of sludge baking in the hot water heat exchangers.

In the UK, pasteurisation is a more recent process and the competitors are preparing to get their share of a growing, but still indecisive market. Most of the systems on the market are pre-pasteurisation, rather than post-pasteurisation systems. The rationale is that pasteurised sludge passed into digestion leaves the digesters with a high concentration of associated micro-organisms, which makes competition for substrate by any invading pathogens much more difficult.

Table 5 presents the different options available on the market. All the processes have proved to reduce efficiently the pathogen content of sewage sludges.

### 4.2.3. Other competitive technologies
The third draft of the Working document on sludge (3) defines an exhaustive list of sludge treatment processes that will achieve an advanced treated sludge standard. They are thermal drying, thermophilic aerobic stabilisation, thermophilic anaerobic digestion, thermal treatment of liquid (pasteurisation), and lime stabilisation. The draft of the UK Code of Practice is less restrictive since it only gives a list of examples of effective conventional treatment.

It was interesting to make a cost comparison between the PUR*iser* and what we considered as being the most competitive technologies, i.e., drying and lime stabilisation.

### 4.2.3.1. Dryers
Sludge drying is a unit operation that involves reducing the water content of a dewatered sludge by vaporisation of water to the air. The moisture content of the dried sludge is less than 10 percent. Different mechanical processes are available for drying sludge. There are indirect, direct and combined dryers systems. The most favoured dryers are the direct type, in particular, the flash dryer, the rotary drum dryer and the belt dryer (5).

Drying is a very flexible process that can be adapted to produce a variety of products suitable for agriculture utilisation, landfill, land reclamation, forestry, fertiliser blending and incineration. It can be used as fuel in gasification plant or industrial boilers for instance. As regards pathogens reduction, drying is a successful post-pasteurisation process because the risk of harmful microbial colonies re-infecting the sludge is limited by reducing the water activity of the product.

**Table 6: Advantages/disadvantages of drying plants**

| Advantages | Disadvantages |
|---|---|
| Reduction in sludge volume | High capital cost |
| The product retains the fertiliser and soil conditioning properties associated with sewage sludge | High operating cost |
| Product suitable for landfill and incineration | Operation is not straightforward |
| Stable product, suitable for long term storage | |

### 4.2.3.2. Stabilisation with Quicklime
Addition of Quicklime (CaO) and/or other alkaline materials as a dry chemical to wet sludge cake produces an enhanced treated product or a conventionally treated product, which are

biologically stable, of high dry solids and reduce odour. The water in the cake slakes the lime, resulting in a considerable evolution of heat. Three disinfection mechanisms are thereby applied:

- high pH (above 12)
- release of free ammonia which acts as a disinfectant (due to high pH)
- rise in temperature to 70 or 80°C due to the heat of hydration of lime (exothermic reaction).

An efficient mixing system is required, using appreciable amounts of energy. The final product of quicklime treatment is relatively dry and easy to handle, the hydration taking up some water and the high temperatures causing some evaporation.
The process suppresses the risk of putrefaction, the emission of volatile sulphides and fatty acids and increases the emission of amines and ammonia. The overall effect is to reduce the offensiveness of the sludge odour, but it is not odourless.

### Table 7: Advantages/disadvantages of liming plants

| Advantages | Disadvantages |
|---|---|
| Low capital costs | High operating costs (lime) |
| Rapid and relatively easy installation | Increased mass of solids in product for disposal |
| Enhance value of the final product | Chemical handling |
| | Odour |

*4.2.3.3. Costs comparison*
Purac have led two parallel studies on lime plants and dryer plants. Suppliers were asked to quote for a drying plant with a sludge throughput of 12,045 tDS/year and for a lime plant with a throughput of 9,440 tDS/year. The capital and operational costs of the technical offers received were analysed and compared to the ones of the PUR*iser*.

The capital prices do not include for civil structure. It is worth noticing that the drying plant will requires a building and the lime plant some odour containment system. The operational costs are based on 4.5 p/kW for the electricity and 80£/tonne of lime.

Five dryers suppliers were contacted and six technical solutions were proposed. The capital price varied between £632,750 and £1,995,000, the average being £1,405,600. The power costs varied between £106,400 and £68,985 a year, the average being £79,103 per year. The less expensive proposal is associated with the most costly power consumption.

The design of the liming plant aims at achieving a log 2 reduction of E.coli and not an advanced treated sludge. For a further pathogen reduction (log6), capital and operational prices will increase as the consumption of lime increases and special equipments or processing steps are involved. Capital costs were between £149,000 for a progressive cavity mixing pump device up to £441,200 for a typical ploughshare mixer and sludge cake conveyor. The power costs are £5,500 for this latter and up to £9,000 per year for the pumping unit.

For the ease of comparison with the PUR*iser*, all the costs were converted into £/tonne dry solids of sludge. Figures 7 and 8 show the capital and operational costs of the drying plant, of the liming plant and of the PUR*iser*. The PURiser costs are plotted against the yearly tonne dry solids throughput of the plant. The data points above 12,000 tDS/year and 9,000 tDS/year represent the dryer and liming plants costs.

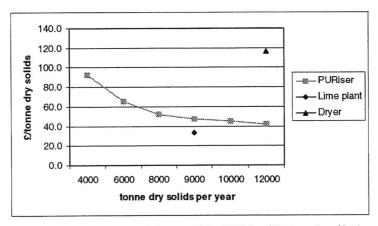

**Figure 7: Comparison of the capital costs of the PURiser/ liming plant/drying plant**

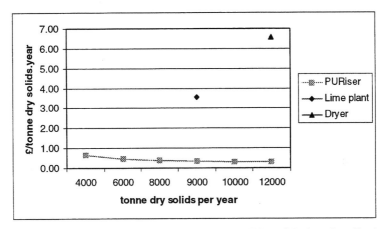

**Figure 8: Comparison of the operational costs of the PUR*iser*/ liming plant/drying plant**

The capital and operational costs of drying plant are far greater than for a PUR*iser* plant. The Capex is 116.7 £/tDS instead of 41.6 £/tDS and the Opex is 6.57 £/tDS.year instead of 0.3 £/DS.year with the PUR*iser*.

The lime stabilisation capital costs are better than for a PUR*iser* plant: 33.41£/tDS instead of 47.5£/tDS. But two remarks must be done. Firstly, the design was based on a log2 reduction of E.coli, the capital costs will increase if a log6 reduction is required for advanced treated sludge. Secondly, the figure has been driven low by the price of the liming progressive cavity pumping system. There is no guarantee that this system will be selected when it comes to achieving a log6 reduction.

The Opex is ten time higher with the lime system, even for a log2 reduction: 3.57 £/tDS.year instead of 0.34 £/tDS.year with the PUR*iser*.

## 5. CONCLUSIONS

The PUR*iser* pasteurisation process has proved its efficiency in removing pathogens from sewage sludge. It complies with the likely future regulations for advanced sludge treatments:

- it can easily achieve a Log6 reduction of <u>E.coli</u>
- it reduces Salmonella and <u>E.coli</u> to levels barely detectable in the pasteurised
- sludge
- it guarantees a minimum retention time at temperature for the sludge

The plant has proved to be reliable and simple to operate. It has little impact on odour generation. It has also been successfully commissioned prior to its installation at Lowestoft during this very fast track program, which overall ran 10 months from project approval through commissioning, testing and decommissioning.

The design of the PUR*iser* has subsequently been optimised. We believe it offers a simple, reliable and competitive technology when compared to dryers or lime stabilisation plants. The PUR*iser* is now entering its commercialisation phase and one plant has already been ordered by Anglian Water (see figure10, Caister installation).

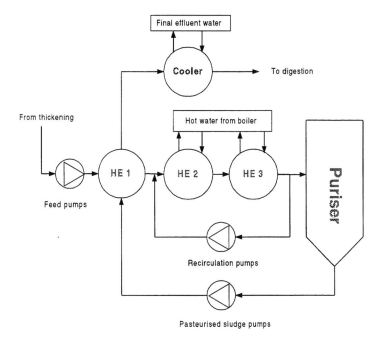

**Figure 9: Schematic of the PUR*iser* pasteurisation plant (Lowestoft installation)**

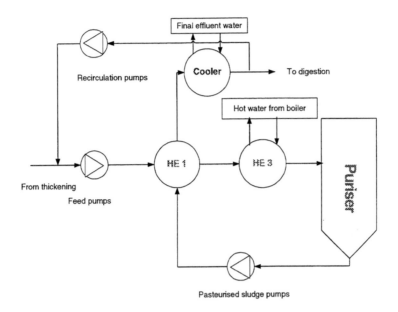

**Figure 10: Schematic of the PUR*iser* pasteurisation plant (Caister installation)**

**REFERENCES**

1.  DEPARTEMENT OF ENVIRONMENT, *Revised UK Code of Practice for Agricultural Use of Sewage Sludge*, Draft of August 2000.

2.  WATER UK AND BRITISH RETAIL CONSORTIUM, *ADAS Environmental*, 1999.

3.  EUROPEAN COMMISSION, *Working Document on Sludge 3rd Draft*, January 2000.

4.  KERN D.Q., Process Heat Transfer, pp 85-101, 1950.

5.  AQUA ENVIRO SLUDGE MASTER CLASS, *Sludge Drying Technology*, February 2001.

# Securing and managing agricultural outlets for biosolids using geographical software on a mobile system

*John Hodson [1] & Bill Griffiths [2]*
[1] *Tynemarch Systems Engineering Ltd.* [2] *Southern Water Services Ltd.*
© Tynemarch Systems Engineering Ltd 2001

## ABSTRACT

Geographical Information System (GIS) software is being run on laptop PCs, enabling advisors to discuss biosolids applications with farmers on site. Field and agricultural unit boundaries are readily digitised, and the amount of biosolids which may be applied is calculated. The software is used to manage the whole process, from producing instructions for spreading including maps, application rates and advice, to recording an audit trail of applications. Mobile use is made possible by transfer of these data via email to and from a central administration site. The software is used to aid identification of new agricultural outlets using mapping overlaid with boundaries of environmental areas, and to identify existing outlets due to be re-contacted.

## 1   INTRODUCTION

It is well recognised that new agricultural and other beneficial outlets must be secured in order to handle the greater volumes of biosolids produced as a result of the Urban Wastewater Treatment Directive. To achieve this not only must suitable outlets be located but a highly professional approach must be demonstrated to farmers to satisfy them that application of biosolids will be conducted within all appropriate safeguards and will protect their future interests. Finally, there is an ever-present requirement to conduct operations more cost-effectively.

This paper describes the ways in which computer systems can be employed to address these issues. A fully-integrated system has been developed to aid management of the recycling operation from locating new outlets, through to providing advice and instructions on allowable application volumes, and to recording and reporting on applications made. Experience of using this system has demonstrated where benefits are to be gained, not only from the facilities offered by the system but also in the new field-based ways of working which the system enables.

## 2   GEOGRAPHICAL INFORMATION SYSTEMS (GIS)

### 2.1   Replacement and enhancement of current methods

A number of tasks previously carried out on paper have been enhanced by the provision of a GIS interface to display maps and edit geographical information.

Every advisor has available the up-to-date Ordnance Survey mapping for the whole region. This mapping was readily obtainable from existing corporate sources in two levels of detail: 1:2,500 detailed 'vector' maps and 1:50,000 overview 'raster' maps.

The vector mapping is composed of lines showing field boundaries, watercourses and so on, and may be displayed at any scale required. The watercourse lines are captured by the software and used to generate default restricted areas within which biosolids may not be applied. The on-screen display is shown in Figure 1.

The raster mapping is a bitmap image of smaller-scale printed maps, and is useful to provide an overview display of wider areas. There are several alternative ways of finding the required area on the map: a town/street gazetteer, National Grid Reference, or selection of a previously digitised farm/field. The usual facilities are provided to pan around the map once in the general area.

Maps of a number of types of environmental areas were also obtained, such as groundwater protection zones, SSSIs, nitrate vulnerable zones and so on. A key benefit of the GIS system has been the ability to display up-to-date versions of all the different environmental areas at once and in place on the background map. This ensures that the advisor is aware of the presence of these areas and also enables restricted areas to be automatically generated, according to area type.

The software has been developed to enable boundaries such as fields and agricultural units (AUs) to be digitised rapidly and accurately. To this end boundaries can be created by simply clicking on the map, and any adjustments can be made by adding or subtracting further areas. Boundaries are automatically made to fit, for example any overlap with adjacent fields or AUs is removed.

The GIS system avoids the need for copies of farm maps to be kept on paper at an administration site and taken out when required. Definitive copies are always available: updated maps and backup copies are easily distributed to administration and to other advisors, via email. The maps may also be reproduced to any scale on-site, using portable colour printers.

### 2.2   New facilities

In addition to aiding tasks previously carried out, the GIS interface has also enabled a number of new tasks not previously practical.

The ability to display information from all farms alongside each other on the map, at any required scale and level of detail, enables visual inspection to analyse, for example, existing biosolids usage and cropping. It also aids the search for additional landbank in suitable areas according to proximity to the production works and presence of environmental areas.

Geographical calculations become possible, such as automatically determining which works producing a particular type of biosolid are closest to a farm of interest. The GIS system also calculates the nett area of the fields and AUs which have been digitised, taking into account restricted areas to which biosolids may not be applied. Any adjustments to AU and restricted areas necessary for ground slope are made according to the farmer's surveyed field area.

It is also possible to split a field into equal AUs easily and accurately, regardless of the shape of the field. Digitisation directly on top of the Ordnance Survey map ensures that an accurate record is obtained, rather than relying on a farm map which may be somewhat pictorial in nature.

## 3   MANAGEMENT OF APPLICATIONS

### 3.1   Administration and legislative requirements
Integrated with the GIS system is a database of all the information associated with the biosolids recycling operation, such as production works, farms, soil and sludge samples, applications and so on.

Central to the system is software which has been continually developed over nearly ten years to provide the management facilities required in recycling. At the primary level a comprehensive audit record is maintained of applications made. A comprehensive series of specialised reports provides the instructions for spreading including maps, application rates and advice, and reports for the farmer, Ofwat and the Environment Agency.

A key feature of the software is its ability to calculate the amount of biosolids which may be applied in accordance with the relevant legislation, codes of practice and crop requirements. To do this it uses the stored soil and sludge sample data.

### 3.2   Extracting valuable information from data held
Valuable information is stored for audit requirements which can be exploited for use in managing the recycling operation more effectively.

Specialised reports have been created to determine, for example, the remaining life of the existing landbank according to allowable yearly, three-yearly and ten-yearly application rates. Fields due for further applications can similarly be identified so that farmers can be contacted pro-actively. It is also possible to select a particular biosolids source to suit the soil concentration of potentially toxic elements.

In addition to these specialised reports it is considered essential to have a completely flexible and easy-to-use ad-hoc report generator to extract any other general information required. This facility is used widely, to search for data and to provide summarised information. It enables detailed enquiries from, for example, the Environment Agency to be dealt with effectively from a centralised administration office without relying on familiarity with particular farms at a level only possessed by individual advisors. The data in reports may also be extracted to a spreadsheet, for further manipulation if required.

## 4 MOBILE OPERATION

A fundamental driver in the design of the system was the desire to have the full capabilities available in the field, on laptop PCs.

Firstly this enables a professional approach to be displayed to the customer, providing all the information required to make the sales case, and providing reassurance that the necessary legislation and codes of practice will be taken into account and that the application operation will be accurately guided.

Secondly, as information is entered directly into the system at the time of the site visit it is ensured that it is accurate and not mis-transcribed, that the advisor is fully aware of all environmental constraints and that any additional information required is sought.

A third benefit is the efficiency gain where advisors do not have to be office-based, but can spend more time in the field.

This field-based method of working is made possible by the rapid transfer of data updates between advisors and a central administration site using email. Administration is responsible for managing the soil and sludge sample data, and these are sent to advisors. When these are received the system automatically imports the data from the email and updates any soil condition calculations accordingly. Revised farm details are sent from the advisor to neighbouring advisors and to administration, to enable monitoring of activities and to provide data backups.

This way of working has been proved in practice to have considerable advantages over the previous method where use of the supporting system was limited to visiting the office.

## 5 KEY BENEFITS

Experience in the field has demonstrated many practical benefits of the new system which fall into two key categories: geographical information and streamlined, field-based operation. These are summarised below.

Geographical information benefits:
- Ordnance Survey maps centred on any area are easy to locate and display at a variety of scales
- up-to-date environmental boundaries are readily distributed to every advisor, and overlay the maps exactly
- definitive and accurate field and AU boundary records are rapidly created
- the size of the application area is accurately calculated taking proper account of restricted areas
- existing customer farms and their application patterns may be viewed and analysed en-bloc
- potential new customer farms can be analysed for suitability, and viewed in relation to the location of biosolids production works

Mobile operation benefits:

- a professional approach is displayed to the customer
- advisors are fully aware of all appropriate environmental factors and previous applications
- information is gathered and entered directly and efficiently
- advisors do not have to spend unnecessary time visiting an office simply to consult or update records
- central administration can still monitor operations, analyse information and deal effectively with enquiries from the Environment Agency

Alongside these features of the new system stands its integration with the core database system, combining the following facilities:

- audit record for applications, samples and all associated data
- calculation of compliant application volumes and soil condition
- specialised reports
- ad-hoc reports and data output to spreadsheets
- analysis of customers to be re-contacted, of remaining landbank etc.

## 6   CONCLUSIONS

Many wastewater service providers are still using a mix of computer-based and manual systems to meet their requirements. Typically a cumbersome centralised computer system is used to record applications made, and essential farm maps are recorded on an assorted collection of outline maps held as single file copies. Not only is a large amount of manual effort spent in the flow of information required to manage the overall recycling process, but the service provided to customers is hampered.

In the future it will become increasingly necessary to be able to demonstrate a high quality professional service to existing customers, to locate and secure new customers, and to demonstrate rigorous compliance to other parties such as the Environment Agency.

To meet these needs a fully-integrated software system has been developed. This system has demonstrated that significant benefits can be gained by moving to the field-based way of working which it enables. A range of advances have also been made in the ways in which geographical information is recorded, processed and transmitted.

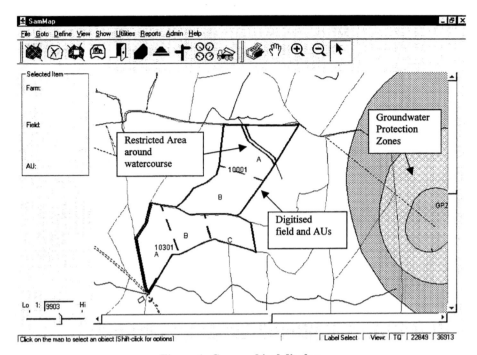

**Figure 1: Geographical display**

# Developments with the "Safe Sludge Matrix" and the use of sewage sludge on land used to grow industrial crops

G A W Hickman[1] and B J Chambers[2]
[1]ADAS Environment, Mamhead Castle, Mamhead, Exeter, EX6 8HD, UK
[2]ADAS Gleadthorpe Research Centre, Meden Vale, Mansfield, NG20 9PF, UK

## 1    ABSTRACT

The landmark agreement between Water UK representing the Water Industry and the British Retail Consortium representing the major retailers in September 1998, resulted in the production of the "Safe Sludge Matrix" (commonly referred to as the ADAS Matrix), which has transformed sewage sludge (biosolids) recycling practices to agricultural land.

The Matrix consists of a table of crops and levels of sewage sludge treatment, with guidance on the treatment level acceptable for each crop type. The 'Matrix' agreement is currently being incorporated into the revised Sludge (Use in Agriculture) Regulations (England) and DETR Code of Practice for Agricultural Use of Sewage Sludge. Similar revisions are also planned by the Scottish Executive, National Assembly for Wales and Department of the Environment in Northern Ireland.

These regulations will define the standards of treatment ("Treated Sludge" and "Enhanced Treated Sludge") referred to in the Matrix, in terms of pathogen reduction levels and end product standards. E.coli has been chosen as the indicator organism, with the standards likely to consist of two elements. Firstly, the treatment process must be fully auditable and be capable of reducing any E.coli that may be present in the sludge by 2 log and 6 log, respectively. Secondly, there is likely to be a maximum allowable concentration, above which it will not be possible to recycle sludge to agricultural land. The hazard analysis and critical control point approach to pathogen risks will be adopted, to audit the critical controls in each treatment process.

The impacts of the "Safe Sludge Matrix" and the proposed changes in legislation have had a profound impact on sludge recycling to agricultural land. As a direct result of the Matrix, all untreated sludges have been banned from application to land used to grow food or animal feed crops since 31st December 1999. The Director General of Water Services at OFWAT announced in 1999 that Water Companies would need to spend £403 million between 2000-2005 to improve sewage sludge recycling, recovery and disposal, much of this being new treatment processes in order to phase out the use of untreated sludge.

The new agreement on recycling untreated sewage sludge to land used to grow specified industrial crops and typical nutrient requirements for a range of crops is also outlined.

## 2 INTRODUCTION

In the region of 515,000 tonnes of sewage sludge dry solids (ds) were recycled to 80,000 ha agricultural land in 1996/97, at an average application rate of 6.4 tds/ha.[1] These quantities compare with around 16 million tonnes of farm manure ds and 4 million tonnes fresh weight of industrial 'wastes'. (Table 1).

Recycling to agricultural land is generally recognised as the Best Practicable Environmental Option (BPEO) for utilising the properties of sludge, enabling its nutrient and organic matter content to be used in supplying crop nutrient requirements and maintaining soil fertility. Sludge provides a useful source of plant available nitrogen (N), phosphorus (P), sulphur (S) and magnesium (Mg), and as a result of some treatment processes may have value as a liming material. The organic matter content also has value as a soil conditioner, improving the structural stability and water holding capacity of soils, especially where applied as a cake.

**Table 1 Estimated quantities of organic manures recycled annually to land in the UK**

| Manure type | Fresh weight | Dry solids |
|---|---|---|
| | (million tonnes) | |
| Sewage sludge | - | 0.5 |
| Farm manures: | | |
| Cattle | 73.3 | 12.0 |
| Pig | 10.4 | 1.0 |
| Poultry | 4.4 | 2.1 |
| Sheep | 2.6 | 0.6 |
| Total | 90.7 | 15.7 |
| Industrial 'wastes' | 3.8 | - |

Sludge applications to land are regulated by European Community Directive 86/278/EEC which has been implemented in England, Scotland and Wales by The Sludge (Use in Agriculture) Regulations 1989 and as amended by The Sludge (Use in Agriculture) Regulations 1990[2]. These are complemented by the DETR Code of Practice for Agricultural Use of Sewage Sludge[3], MAFF Codes of Good Agricultural Practice for the Protection of Water, Soil and Air[4,5&6], and the Prevention of Environmental Pollution from Agricultural Activity - A Code of Practice[7]. In operational practice, sludge use on agricultural land needs to comply the MAFF Water Code recommendation that applications should not supply more than 250 kg total N per hectare per annum, which in most situations will provide the working limit on major nutrient and heavy metal rates.

The landmark agreement between Water UK representing the Water Industry and the British Retail Consortium (BRC) representing the major retailers in September 1998, resulted in the production of the "Safe Sludge Matrix"[8] (commonly referred to as the ADAS Matrix), which has transformed sewage sludge (biosolids) recycling practices to agricultural land.

## 3    BACKGROUND

The health scares over salmonella, listeria, BSE and then *E. Coli* O157 raised public concern over the safe production of food, and because of possible public perception concerns, led the supermarkets to question the long-term sustainability of sourcing food supplies from land receiving sewage sludge. At the same time the Water Industry had to implement the EC Urban Waste Water Treatment Directive[9] which was forecast double the amount of sewage sludge recycled to agricultural land by 2006.

The recycling of sludge to land is considered by Government to be the Best Practicable Environmental Option (BPEO) in most cases. Although other alternatives, such as landfilling and incineration (sometimes involving energy recovery through combustion, pyrolysis or gasification) are available, these are not always consistent with the Government's Waste Strategy and there are public pressures on the incineration route.

In the summer of 1997 when these issues were first aired, some retailers and processors started to review their sourcing of produce from land receiving sludge. Farmers and growers were also worried whether or not the use of sludge was acceptable under the Assured Combinable Crops Scheme (ACCS), Scottish Quality Cereals (SQC) scheme provisions and the various livestock assurance schemes such as Farm Assured British Beef and Lamb (FABBL).

ADAS were subsequently commissioned to assist in managing the negotiations between Water UK representing the Water Industry and the BRC representing the major retailers. The aim was to secure a sustainable route for recycling sewage sludge to agricultural land that was acceptable to the Food Industry, Water Industry, Regulators and of course farmers and growers.

Following a year of intensive consultation and discussion between the two parties, with input from the Environment Agency (EA), Department of Environment Transport and Regions (DETR) and Ministry of Agriculture Fisheries and Food (MAFF), including discussions with other stakeholders, such as the National Farmers Union (NFU), Country Landowners Association (CLA), food manufacturers and food processors, agreement was reached in September 1998. The agreement resulted in the production of the "Safe Sludge Matrix", commonly known as the ADAS Matrix, which has been accepted as the minimum standard for sustainable sludge recycling to agricultural land.

## 4    THE "SAFE SLUDGE MATRIX"

The Matrix consists of a table of crops and levels of sewage sludge treatment (Table 2), with guidance on the treatment level acceptable for each crop type. The 'Matrix' agreement is being incorporated into the revised Sludge (Use in Agriculture) Regulations (England) and DETR Code of Practice for Agricultural Use of Sewage Sludge, both due to be revised during 2001. Similar revisions are also planned by the Scottish Executive (SE), National Assembly for Wales (NAW) and Department of the Environment in Northern Ireland (DoE).

## Table 2. The "Safe Sludge Matrix"

| Crop Group | Untreated Sludges | Conventionally Treated Sludges | Enhanced Treated Sludges |
|---|---|---|---|
| FRUIT | X | X | ✓ (1) |
| SALAD | X | X<br>(30 month harvest interval applies) | ✓ (1) |
| VEGETABLES | X | X<br>(12 month harvest interval applies) | ✓ (1) |
| HORTICULTURE | X | X | ✓ (1) |
| COMBINABLE & ANIMAL FEED CROPS | X | ✓ | ✓ |
| GRASS & FORAGE  -GRAZED | X | X (2)<br>(Deep injected or ploughed down only) | ✓ (2) |
| -HARVESTED | X | ✓ (2) | ✓ (2) |

✓ All applications must comply with the Sludge (Use in Agriculture) Regulations and DETR Code of Practice for Agricultural Use of Sewage Sludge (to be revised during 2001)

X Applications not allowed (except where stated conditions apply).

(1) 10 month harvest interval applies

(2) 3 week no grazing and harvest interval applies

The revised regulations will define the standards of treatment ("Conventionally Treated Sludge" and "Enhanced Treated Sludge") referred to in the Matrix, in terms of pathogen reduction levels and end product standards. *E.coli* has been chosen as the indicator organism, with the standards likely to consist of two elements. Firstly, the treatment process must be fully auditable and be capable of reducing any *E.coli* that may be present in the sludge by 2 log (99% reduction) and 6 log (99.9999% reduction), respectively. Secondly, there is likely to be a maximum allowable concentration (MAC), above which it will not be possible to recycle sludge to agricultural land. The MAC proposed for conventionally treated sludge is $10^5$ *E.coli* per gram ds and for enhanced treated sludge the proposed MAC is $10^3$ *E.coli* per gram ds. Enhanced Treated sludges will also need to be sampled to confirm the absence of *Salmonella spp.* in five random samples each containing 2 grams dry solids. Transitional arrangements using a 90 percentile for conventionally treated sludge MAC have also been proposed.

The hazard analysis and critical control point (HACCP) approach to pathogen risks will be adopted, to audit the critical controls in each treatment process.

## 5   MAIN IMPACTS OF THE MATRIX

The main impact of the 'Matrix' has been the phasing out of untreated sewage sludge use on agricultural land. The application of raw or untreated sludge has been banned on grazing land, land used to grow grass/maize silage, fruit, vegetables and salad crops since 31st December 1998, and from all land used to grow food crops from 31st December 1999. The use of untreated sludge will be phased out on land used to grow industrial crops that also have a food use from 31st December 2001, and on certain specified non-food crops from 31 December 2005. From the latter date the use of all untreated sludge will be prohibited on agricultural land.

The surface spreading of conventionally treated sludge (previously referred to as treated sludge) on grazed grassland was banned from the 31st December 1998. Conventionally Treated sludge can only be applied to grazed grassland where it is deep injected or ploughed in/ deep incorporated prior to establishing a new grass ley. Conventionally treated sludge can be applied to the surface of grassland or for forage crops such as maize, which will subsequently be harvested, but there can be no grazing of that land within the season of application (i.e. it is not permissible to graze any grass regrowth or aftermath in the season that the sludge was applied).

Conventionally treated sludge may still be applied to land growing vegetable and salad crops in rotation, provided that at least 12 months have elapsed between application to land and the harvest of the following field vegetable crop. Where the crop is one which might be eaten raw (e.g. a salad crop), the harvest interval must be at least 30 months.

The agreement also introduced a new class of treatment, *"Enhanced Treated"*(originally referred to as Advanced Treated), to describe treatment processes which are capable of virtually eliminating any pathogens which may be present in the original sludge. This was the first time in the UK that there had been recognition of differences in effectiveness of treatment methods, parallels can be drawn with the United States of America Environmental Protection Agency (EPA) standards which differentiate between Class A and Class B sludge products. The EU are now also proposing to adopt a 'Matrix' type approach and are proposing two standards in the 3rd Working Draft of the proposed revision to the Sludge Directive[10].

## 6   ONGOING DEVELOPMENTS

A steering group drawn from Water UK, BRC, Food and Drink Federation (FDF), DETR, Food Standards Agency (FSA) and the EA, chaired by ADAS, has been set up to continue the development and evaluation of research information. The Water Industry needs to be able to demonstrate to key stakeholders, that treatment methods are effective and that the standards in the "Matrix" are being achieved from treatment through to application. More importantly, the onus is on the Water Industry to be pro-active in demonstrating compliance and in developing innovative and safer practices, and widening their customer base for the beneficial use of treated biosolids.

Ongoing research includes an assessment of the efficacy of sewage treatment processes on pathogens (led by Leeds University) and a risk assessment of recycling sewage sludge to agricultural land (led by WRc). The Research Steering Group meets regularly and is a valuable forum to discuss and debate key issues affecting all aspects of the treatment and application of sludge to agricultural land.

Sewerage operators, process operators and suppliers of equipment are currently looking at the principles of HACCP, as a means of monitoring processes and providing the evidence to show that the treatment processes are achieving the required level of pathogen kill. Processes such as thermal drying, composting, alkaline stabilisation/pasteurisation and some pre-digestion pasteurisation treatments are likely to be acceptable as Enhanced treatment methods. But each individual process will need to demonstrate that it is consistently capable of producing a 'hygienised' or 'sanitised' product, and in particular that the process will deliver a 6 log reduction of a range of pathogens, and specifically $E.coli$. This may need to involve 'spiking' the influent raw sludge since many pathogens are not found in sufficient quantities to be able to demonstrate that the process is capable of a 6 log reduction.

The provisions of the "Safe Sludge Matrix" are regularly assessed, and during the most recent review the issues associated with the recycling of untreated sludge to agricultural land were addressed by the Research Steering Group. It was accepted that there are major perception issues associated with recycling untreated sludge, however, there was also evidence that recycling untreated sludge to land can provide additional benefits to the soil and water environment compared to conventionally or enhanced treated sludges.

The benefits arise from the fact that untreated sludge has a higher concentration of organic matter and is a better source of slow release nitrogen. The nitrogen is largely held in the organic fraction rather than in the liquid phase and compared with liquid digested sludges, is potentially less prone to leaching loss in the short term. Treatment of sludge also results in some concentration of heavy metals in the dry solids. Processing of sewage sludge and the resultant effluents and liquors has an energy demand and unless the biogas produced from digestion is converted to energy, untreated sludges have a lower net energy usage than digested products.

Under AMP3 determinations funding has been provided to the Industry for sludge treatment. Investment should be complete by 2005. Provided adequate safeguards were established to ensure that the risk of pathogen transfer to food crops was removed, it was proposed, subject to review, that a outlet for untreated sludges, onto genuine non-food crops would be permitted until the end of 2005.

# 7  USE OF SEWAGE SLUDGE ON INDUSTRIAL CROPS

## 7.1  Nutrient requirements of industrial crops

Government strategy on New and Renewable Energy has set targets of 10% electricity generation from Renewable Resources by 2010. It is expected that biomass will have an important contribution to play in the achievement of these targets. Sewage sludges (biosolids) represent an important source of nutrients to growing crops, with the recycling of biosolids to land leading to the recovery and utilisation of these nutrients.

The area of biomass crops represents a useful opportunity to beneficially recycle nutrients in an acceptable and environmentally responsible way. Many biomass crops are grown or poor quality or restored land and in such situations, the beneficial soil conditioning properties of biosolids are particularly valuable.

The response of biomass crops to applied fertilisers and nutrient inputs is an important factor in evaluating their suitability for recycling biosolids. Typically biomass crops have relatively low nutrient demands, which can be a barrier to the use of biosolids as the aim is to meet and not exceed crop needs, so as to minimise the risk of nutrient run-off or leaching. More is known about the nutrient requirements of High Erucic Acid Rape (HEAR) and Hemp, as they already in commercial production. Typical requirements are higher for these annual crops than for perennial biomass crops such as Miscanthus and short rotation coppice (SRC), Table 3.

### Table 3 Typical  annual nutrient requirements of specified industrial crops

| Industrial crop | Typical  annual nutrient requirements (kg/ha)[*] | | |
|---|---|---|---|
| | Nitrogen | Phosphate | Potash |
| Short rotation coppice (SRC) | 20-80 | 20-80 | 20-100 |
| Miscanthus | 25-100 | 5-20 | 20-100 |
| HEAR | 120-150 | 50 | 50 |
| Hemp | 120 | 50 | 50 |

Source: Christian & Bullard[11]

(*) Requirement varies with stage of establishment/maturity and time of establishment

It should, however, be stressed that there is still relatively little experimental data available for most biomass crops grown in the UK, and it is possible that crops will respond to higher rates of applied nutrients than shown in Table 3.

The other area requiring further research relates to application techniques, particularly for untreated sewage sludge, where the material must be deep injected or incorporated into the soil. Applications to established perennial crops with woody rooting systems such as SRC are potentially difficult, and it is not yet known whether disturbance to the rhizomes of crops such as Miscanthus will result in a shortening of productive life. Applications to annual crops are not thought likely to present any problems.

## 7.2 Industrial crop agreement

Following discussions with key stakeholders, it has been agreed that untreated sewage sludge can continue to be recycled to agricultural land used to grow specified industrial crops until 31 December 2005. Also, suitable audit procedures will also need to be followed to ensure that no products from the industrial crop enter the food chain. Details of the agreement are summarised in Table 4 and can be found in "Guidelines for the Application of Sewage Sludge to Industrial Crops"[12].

**Table 4 Summary of specified crops suitable to receive untreated sewage sludge**

| Industrial Crop | Treated and Enhanced Treated Sludge | Untreated Sludge | |
|---|---|---|---|
| Willow & Poplar grown for coppicing | ✓ * | ✓ | To end 31/12/2005 |
| Miscanthus for biomass | ✓ * | ✓ | Subject to the agreed harvest intervals |
| Hemp for fibre | ✓ * | ✓ | To end 31/12/2005 |
| High Erucic Acid Rape (HEAR) for production of High Erucic Acid Rape Oil (HERO) | ✓ * | ✓ | Crops to be grown under contract and auditable protocols in place to guarantee none of the crop enters the human or animal feed chain and subject to the agreed harvest intervals |
| Industrial Oilseed Rape | ✓ * | ✗ | |
| Linseed | ✓ * | ✗ | Not permitted from 31/12/2001, even if grown under contract for non-food use. |
| Flax | ✓ * | ✗ | |
| Others- including:- spurge, pyrethrum, kenaf, cotton, nettle, pot marigold, calendula, woad, reeds, cordgrass etc. | ✓ * | ✗ | Not permitted at present. However new commercial crops that have no food use may be acceptable in the future, subject to agreement. |

✓ All applications must comply with the Sludge (Use in Agriculture) Regulations and Code of Practice for Agricultural Use of sewage Sludge.

\* Subject to the harvest intervals specified in the Safe Sludge Matrix

✗ Applications not allowed

Applications of untreated sludge will also be subject to increased harvest intervals between application of the sludge and harvest of a subsequent food crop. The harvest intervals are 18 months for a combinable or animal feed crop, 36 months for vegetables and forage crops, and 48 months for salad and horticultural crops. Harvest intervals for conventionally treated and enhanced treated products are detailed in the "Safe Sludge Matrix".

## 8   CONCLUSIONS

The impacts of the "Safe Sludge Matrix" and the proposed changes in legislation have had a profound impact on sludge recycling to agricultural land. As a direct result of the Matrix, all untreated sludges have been banned from application to land used to grow food or animal feed crops since 31$^{st}$ December 1999.

The cost to the Water Industry of complying with the agreement will be significant, although the amount will vary from company to company depending on the amount of sludge that is produced, the existing levels of treatment and application methods used. The Director General of Water Services at OFWAT announced in 1999 that Water Companies would need to spend £403 million between 2000-2005 to improve sewage sludge recycling, recovery and disposal, much of this being new treatment processes in order to phase out the use of untreated sludge.

The Water Industry now has a more secure and sustainable route for recycling sludge to agricultural land. Farmers and growers can utilise the beneficial properties in sludge as a valuable and cost effective source of nutrients and organic matter.

The industrial crops agreement has maintained the outlet for untreated sludge, including material that fails the end product standards for pathogens from conventional treatment processes until 2005, and may well help stimulate the development of biomass and other specified industrial crops in the UK.

## 9   REFERENCES

(1)   Gendebien, A., Carlton-Smith, C., Izzu, M and Hall, J.E (1998). *UK Sludge Survey - National Presentation*. Environment Agency Final Technical Report. P165.

(2)   United Kingdom Statutory Instrument No. 880.(1990) *The Sludge (Use in Agriculture) (Amendment) Regulations, 1990*. HMSO, London.

(3)   DoE (1990) *Code of Practice for the Agricultural Use of Sewage Sludge*. Department of Environment. HMSO, London. Available from DETR Publications.

(4)   MAFF (1998) *Code of Good Agricultural Practice for the Protection of Water MAFF/WOAD*. MAFF Publications, London. (PB0587).

(5)   MAFF (1998). *Code of Good Agricultural Practice for the Protection of Air. MAFF/WOAD*. MAFF Publications, London. (PB0618).

(6)   MAFF (1998). *Code of Good Agricultural Practice for the Protection of Soil. MAFF/WOAD*. MAFF Publications, London. (PB0617).

(7)   SOAFED (1997). *Prevention of environmental pollution from Agricultural Activity. A code of practice*. Edinburgh, HMSO.

(8)   ADAS/BRC/Water UK (2001). *The Safe Sludge Matrix – Guidelines for the Application of Sewage Sludge to Agricultural Land* – 3$^{rd}$ Edition.. ADAS 2001.

(9)   EC (1994). *Urban Waste Water Treatment Directive (91/271/EEC)*. Official Journal of the    European Community, L135.

(10)  EU (2000). *Working Document on Sludge – 3$^{rd}$ Draft*. ENV.E  Brussels 2000.

(11)  Christian, D G, Bullard, M J & Wilkins, C (1997) *The Agronomy of some Herbaceous Crops Grown for Energy in Southern England*. Aspects of Applied Biology, 49, pp 41-53.

(12)  ADAS/BRC/Water UK (2001), *Guidelines for the Application of Sewage Sludge to Industrial Crops*. ADAS 2001.

# The increasing importance of assessing toxicity in determining sludge health and management policy

P. Spencer Davies and Fiona Murdoch,
Strathkelvin Instruments Limited
1.05 Kelvin Campus, West of Scotland Science Park, Glasgow, G20 0SP

## SYNOPSIS

The harm caused by toxic industrial effluents to sewage treatment works, has been recognised for many years. These can cause reduction in biodegradable efficiency, with an associated requirement for longer treatment time, and in extreme cases, toxic shock can kill off the secondary tanks.

Currently, the presence of harmful industrial effluents is made evident by their effects on the overall treatment cycle at the works. An increasing frequency of incidents has led to a call to establish or improve methods of detecting toxicity of effluents accepted for treatment.

This paper describes the causes and effects, discusses economic and operational penalties, and reviews the current approach to, and methods of detection. The paper ends with an appraisal of the likely advances over the next few years and the ways in which improved detection can lead to a toxicity management strategy for the operation of sewage treatment works.

## INTRODUCTION

The effective management of the activated sludge of a biological treatment plant is of critical importance in order to minimise treatment costs and to avoid contamination by effluents of receiving waters. Even in well managed treatment systems, it is not uncommon for influent characteristics to change rapidly and unexpectedly as a result of changes in upstream discharges. Plants that treat industrial waste may find that toxic or inhibitory chemicals can pass through treatment systems with little effective removal (1,2,3). Storm flows can introduce toxins from leachates and other urban runoffs. The reduction of treatment plant efficiency resulting from the effects of toxicity on the activated sludge bacteria can therefore result in unacceptable levels of effluent toxicity.

Toxicity can also give rise to operational problems such as changes to the sludge settling characteristics, and this may take a significant time to recover. Settling problems can be caused by both filamentous bulking and by deflocculation. Both of these can be induced by toxic shock loads (4). Filamentous bulking may be detected by microscopic examination, enabling corrective action to be taken. However, the only indication of toxicity-induced deflocculation may be a rapid increase in effluent suspended solids. This may result in significant activated sludge washout before the cause and source of the problem have been identified.

The relationship between the observed consequences of toxicity shocks of this sort and the way in which the toxins affect the metabolic processes of the sludge bacteria is not well understood. This is unfortunate, since toxicity detection methods inevitably have to be based upon knowledge of this sort. The bacteria break down organic compounds in the mixed liquor, thereby reducing BOD and COD. The carbon removed is used either for the respiration of the bacteria or is incorporated into new biomass, as a result of growth. Any stage in the chain of metabolic reactions involved in both respiration and growth, can be poisoned by different toxic chemicals. As the respiration rate and growth rate is inhibited, the rate of breakdown of the carbon compounds of the mixed liquor decreases. As a result, the rate of BOD removal decreases. So toxic shocks can result in increases in effluent BOD and COD levels unless remedial action is taken. Similar effects on the nitrifying bacteria result in increases in ammonia levels in the effluent. In extreme cases the bacteria are killed by the toxicity. The restoration of a plant which has experienced total killoff, involving cleanout and reseeding, is a costly operation.

The role of toxicity management in treatment works is now receiving more attention from plant managers, largely as a result of the introduction of recent environmental legislation. However, there are also good economic and operational reasons for doing this. In this paper procedures and methods which are becoming available for the management of toxicity will be reviewed.

## TOXICITY AND LEGISLATION

Most legislation is directed towards regulation of discharges to the receiving environment, rather than to wastewater treatment works. However, Annex 1 of the EU Urban Waste Water Treatment Directive (1991) states 'Industrial wastewater entering collecting systems and urban waste water treatment plants shall be subject to such pre-treatment as is required in order to: ... - ensure that the operation of the waste water treatment plant and the treatment of sludge are not impeded'. This has been largely overlooked and has not been the subject of secondary legislation, although in the UK some water companies do use toxicity-based discharge consents in some instances.

The more recent EU Water Framework Directive (2000) is concerned primarily with protecting receiving waters from pollution. The scope of regulation will increase beyond existing levels to place more emphasis than hitherto on reduction of toxic chemicals entering receiving waters. Currently some discharge consents are based upon concentration limits of known toxic chemicals. However in recognition of the fact that very often a discharger does not know the exact composition of the waste stream, and also that the toxicity of many of the discharged chemicals is not known, a more pragmatic approach will be used. Using a series of Direct Toxicity Assessment (DTA) tests, the toxicity of end-of-pipe effluents to a series of prescribed organisms from marine or freshwaters, can be measured. Tests of this sort have undergone several years of field trials by the Environment Agency, SEPA and representatives of the chemical industry. Although the date and manner in which these will be used in formulating discharge consents has not yet been announced, it is likely that future IPPC consents will incorporate these DTA tests.

In the United States, the Environmental Protection Agency (EPA) regulates discharges to both receiving waters and to publicly owned treatment works (POTW's). Paradoxically, whilst discharges to receiving waters are subject to direct toxicity testing (Whole Effluent Toxicity or WET tests) the discharge to POTW's is not. The consents for discharge to POTW, which are prescribed in the EPA's National Pretreatment Program (5), are still based upon concentration limits of some 129 registered toxic chemicals.

## TOXICITY EVENTS AND OPERATIONAL CONSEQUENCES

Records of total kill-off of secondary tanks are largely anecdotal. Recently however, instances of partial and chronic toxicity events have appeared in the literature. In Sweden, it was found that 60% of 109 treatment works investigated showed inhibition of nitrification, some with more than 20% inhibition (6). In another study in Greece, up to 50% inhibition of nitrification was attributable to industrial wastewater (7). In the UK, chronic nitrification inhibition levels of approximately 15% were found in a plant receiving a mixture of domestic and industrial waste, with occasional peaks of up to 50% (8).

Whilst nitrification inhibition will have its major effect on the quality of the effluent, with potential consequences for failed discharge consents, respiration inhibition is an indicator of problems with biodegradation of BOD. In Sao Paulo elevated BOD was correlated with filamentous bulking in a treatment plant which received large volumes of industrial waste water (9). The Antwerp treatment works showed almost continuous inhibition of respiration rate of the activated sludge over a 10 day monitoring period. Peaks were up to 30%, with an average of 10% respiration inhibition. No deterioration of effluent quality was observed during this period. However during a second 10 day period, there was a 48 hour increase in toxicity with peaks of up to 43% and this was accompanied by a substantial washout of solids (10).

Computer modelling can be useful in predicting the consequence of toxicity events. A computer model simulation, using the Activated Sludge Model No 1 (11), and process layout and influent pattern of the COST 624 simulation benchmark (12,13,14), was used to model the effects of a non-soluble non-biodegradable toxic substance which caused inhibition of the respiration rate. The model used a treatment plant consisting of 5 completely mixed aeration tanks and a secondary settler. It was found (Figures 1 & 2) that at the lower concentration used in the simulation, there was a 50% decrease in respiration rate and this caused a 3-4 fold increase in the effluent COD. Increasing the toxin concentration fourfold increased the respiration inhibition to approximately 80%, with a consequential increase in effluent COD of 150% (15).

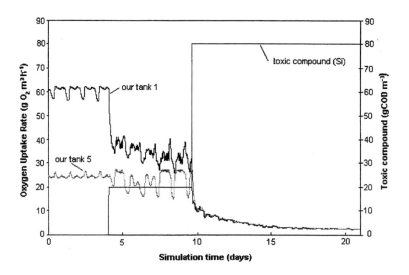

**Figure 1  Computer model simulation of the effect of influent toxicant on respiration rate in 1$^{st}$ and 5$^{th}$ aeration tank (15).**

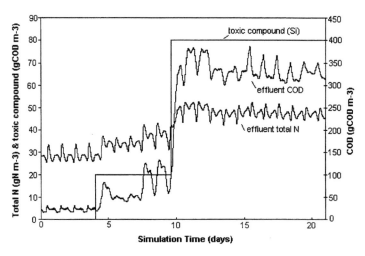

**Figure 2  Computer model simulation of the effect of influent toxicant on effluent N and COD concentrations (15).**

Since respiration inhibition results in a lower rate of breakdown of degradable compounds, this has to be compensated for by an increase in the retention or treatment time, where this is feasible. Aeration costs may increase as a result, although this will to some extent be offset by a lower aeration requirement, as the rate of oxygen consumption by the bacteria decreases. In some European countries charges are levied according to the BOD or COD of the

© BHR Group 2001 Sludge

discharged effluents. In these cases, if retention time cannot be increased in order to keep BOD and COD within limits, there will be increased costs imposed upon the treatment works.

Information on the economic costs of toxicity events at sewage treatment plants is sparse. However, in the Netherlands in the year 2000, a 95000 p.e. municipal plant was subject to a 50% decrease of biomass activity due to an oil spill. The recovery of the plant took 5 days and the costs were approximately 45000 Euros (16). On another occasion, the cost of recovery of an industrial wastewater works treating an average of 1400 $m^3$ $d^{-1}$ of waste from a chemical plant, was reported to be 40,000 Euros (16).

## PROCEDURES FOR TOXICITY MEASUREMENT

There are three main approaches to the measurement of wastewater toxicity: on-line devices; in-situ devices; and laboratory instruments. They have complementary roles in the management of toxicity at treatment plants.

### On-line devices
These attempt to alert the plant operators to the presence of toxic substances in the influent before it is discharged into the plant. This allows diversion of the influent stream to storage tanks, giving time for consideration of whether detoxification can be undertaken or whether to slow-feed the waste into the plant. The role of on-line devices is therefore in protection against unexpected toxic slugs.

Ideally these devices should be continuous, taking measurements in real time. However a number of systems, by the nature of the measurement principle, are discrete-sampling systems. Influent will continue to enter the plant for the length of time required to take the measurement on the sample taken. Since the total amount of toxicity entering during this time will be small in relation to the volume of the receiving tanks, in most cases this is not a serious issue. Examples of on-line monitors are the Rodtox and Stiptox which measure respiration inhibition, and Amtox which measures nitrification inhibition. On-line early warning devices have recently been reviewed by a WERF working party. They evaluated the advantages and disadvantages of the various systems available and made recommendations for their further development (17).

Whilst on-line devices have the benefit of protecting treatment plants from incoming toxicity, those currently available are widely recognised to be prone to false positives. Furthermore they cannot provide information on the nature nor the source of the toxicity. Laboratory tests are therefore required to achieve these.

### In-situ devices
In operational terms, these occupy the niche between on-line and laboratory devices. They sample the actual sludge in the aeration tanks - on a discrete-sampling basis in the case of respirometers - and monitor the presence of toxicity in the tanks. This is a useful approach in that it provides information to the operators which can be used in process control.

### Laboratory instruments
These use batch tests, and ideally should give information on toxicity to the activated sludge bacteria which will receive the waste. Laboratory tests are used for evaluating the toxicity of tankered waste before acceptance for treatment. They should be used, as noted above, in conjunction with on-line devices to check for false alarms, but his is not yet widely practiced.

Laboratory tests may be used in toxicity tracking to locate the source of toxicity, and for evaluation of toxicity of new streams before discharge. Although this is not yet widely practiced, laboratory procedures of this sort could be used as a basis of toxicity-based consents. This would enable the treatment works manager to be aware of the actual toxicity of wastewater which will be received via sewer. It could also be used to determine a treatment cost strategy. The MOGDEN formula currently in use, undoubtedly undercharges a producer of low BOD, but highly toxic and damaging waste. Finally, laboratory instruments can be used to test procedures for reducing the toxicity of highly toxic materials before discharge to sewer.

## PRINCIPLES OF LABORATORY TOXICITY TESTING

The principles involved in three most commonly used groups of laboratory instruments are: bacterial luminescence, nitrification inhibition and activated sludge respiration inhibition. Other procedures involve the use of biosensors (Biosense) and enhanced chemiluminescence of solutions of enzymes in solution (Eclox, Aquanox)

### *Bacterial luminescence*

Here different concentrations of the wastewater are mixed with a culture of a marine luminescent bacterium. The decrease in light output is a measure of toxicity. In principle, this is similar to measuring respiration inhibition, since luminescence is a measure of the rate at which the bacteria produce ATP in the course of their respiratory metabolism. Well known examples of this method are Microtox and Toxalert. The method has the advantage that it has been in use for a long period of time during which a large amount of toxicity data has been generated. However, the test requires expensive consumables, and since it is based upon the luminescence of cultures of a single marine bacterium, it does not provide information on the toxicity to the actual bacteria of the receiving activated sludge. It follows from this that in some instances the test will fail to detect actual toxicity. Of equal importance is that it may be oversensitive to some mildly toxic substances.

### *Nitrification inhibition*

This detects inhibition to the nitrifying bacteria *Nitrobacter* and *Nitrosomonas*, often using pure cultures to achieve this. An example of this is Amtox, which measures changes in the concentration of ammonia resulting form nitrification when the bacteria are incubated with toxic wastewater. Nitrification inhibition is often regarded as a very sensitive test for toxicity, since nitrifying bacteria are generally more prone to poisoning by toxins, and because efficient nitrification is required in order to meet ammonia effluent limits. However, these tests do not provide information on the heterotrophic bacteria which form the bulk of the sludge biomass and which are involved in BOD removal. It follows therefore that in non-nitrifying plants, these tests would have a lack of relevance. Furthermore in many treatment plants, nitrification takes place in tertiary treatment tanks subsequent to BOD removal. In these cases use of nitrification inhibition tests on the influent wastewater entering the treatment works may result in over-estimation of toxicity to the nitrifiers, since some of the toxic substances may be biodegraded in the course of treatment in the secondary tanks.

## ACTIVATED SLUDGE RESPIRATION INHIBITION

These tests measure the inhibition of the total oxygen uptake by the activated sludge bacteria when mixed with toxic wastewater. In sludge from secondary tanks which also nitrify, the

© BHR Group 2001 Sludge

rate of oxygen uptake is a measure of both the respiration of the heterotrophic bacteria and of the oxidative reactions involved with the nitrification of ammonia to nitrite and nitrate. Respiration rate is a measure of the energy metabolism of the bacteria, and most of this energy is used for their biosynthesis and growth. Oxygen uptake rate is therefore a good estimator of the biomass growth rate and of the 'health' of the activated sludge. Both respiration rate and growth rate are also highly correlated with the rate of biodegradation of the complex organic carbon compounds in the sewage.

Respiration inhibition tests, involve the measurement of the concentration of wastewater causing a 50% (or other selected percentage) inhibition of the respiration rate. They are therefore of direct relevance to the processes taking place in the treatment works. Examples of activated sludge respirometers are the Emeris and Strathkelvin ASR, produced in the UK, and several others, of which the Arthur is probably the best known, in the USA.

Although the advantages of respirometry have been well known for some time, activated sludge respiration inhibition tests have not been widely applied. This appears to be due to the commonly held view that respirometry is time-consuming and difficult. This in turn has stemmed from the lack of a dedicated instrument designed for the purpose. Strathkelvin Instruments has now brought to market an Activated Sludge Respirometer which has been designed to offer speed, simplicity and accuracy in operation (Figure 3).

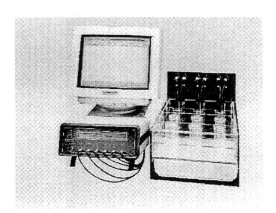

**Figure 3  The Strathkelvin Activated Sludge Respirometer which utilises 6 oxygen electrodes connected via an interface to the pc loaded with dedicated respirometry software.**

The oxygen sensors of the respirometer are Clark-type polarographic electrodes. Other respirometers which have been used for activated sludge have depended upon the use of a single electrode. The associated protocols have involved measurement of the rate of oxygen depletion of a sample of the sludge in a closed container, followed by re-aeration to the starting oxygen level again. This process was repeated several times creating a series of respirograms. The procedure is time-consuming and is not readily adaptable to the measurement of the effects of different concentrations of the wastewater on the sludge respiration rate. The Strathkelvin respirometer results from a technology transfer from respirometry applications in the biomedical field, and uses 6 oxygen electrodes simultaneously. In order to make the instrument compact, sludge sample volumes have been reduced to 20 mls. The variation in respiration rates between 6 samples from the same batch of sludge is very small. The rates measured on these 20 ml samples are almost identical to those measured in a 1 litre sample.

The use of 6 oxygen electrodes enables the respiration rate of a control sample of sludge to be measured at the same time as that of samples of the same sludge mixed with 5 different concentrations of wastewater. Using sludge with a MLSS of approximately 4000 mg/l, the respiration rate of the 6 test samples can be recorded in only 5-10 mins. The dedicated respirometry software allows the analysis of the traces to be carried out automatically at the termination of the run (Figure 4).

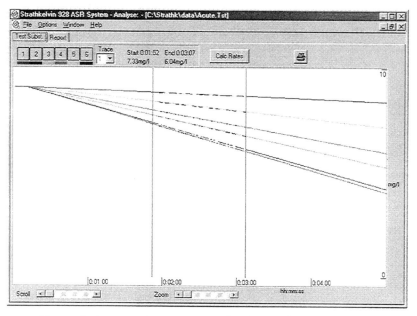

**Figure 4  The analysis screen showing the results of a respirometry run.  Clicking the 'Calc Rates' button transfers the calculated results to the Report page.**

The results of the test are displayed as a fully audited Report in a locked spreadsheet. The report shows values for $EC_5$, $EC_{10}$, $EC_{20}$ and $EC_{50}$ i.e. the concentrations which produce a 5%, 10%, 20% or 50% inhibition of the respiration rate. These values can be used by the treatment plant manager, as shown below, to determine the rate at which the wastewater should be allowed to enter the plant, in order to minimise the effects of toxicity on the activated sludge.

In addition to the toxicity test, the software offers a sludge respirometry test which simply outputs MLSS-normalised respiration rates. These data can be used to check for chronic toxicity in the secondary tanks by daily monitoring of the 'health' of the sludge. The test can also be used to yield data on aeration requirements for process control optimisation.

124                © BHR Group 2001 Sludge

# CASE STUDY OF A RESPIRATION INHIBITION TOXICITY TEST

This example shows the result of a test on tankered waste of unknown composition, which was delivered for treatment at a biological treatment plant.

**Acute test**

| Test substance: | ES Plant | Date: Tue Jan 23 2001 |
|---|---|---|

Control respiration rate

Temperature

20.0 °C

| | Respiration Rate (mg/l/h) |
|---|---|
| Control | 124.5 |

**Test substance:** **ES Plant**
(Datafile: C:\StrathK\Data\testmanual.tst)

Comments: Line 3 effluent

| | Concentration ( % ) | Respiration Rate (mg/l/h) | % Inhibition |
|---|---|---|---|
| Sample 1 | 20 | 120.2 | 3.4 |
| Sample 2 | 40 | 94.4 | 24.1 |
| Sample 3 | 60 | 77.3 | 37.9 |
| Sample 4 | 80 | 47.2 | 62.1 |
| Sample 5 | 100 | 17.2 | 86.2 |

**Concentration causing inhibition of:**
- 5% (EC5) = **21.1** %
- 10% (EC10) = **24.9** %
- 20% (EC20) = **34.8** %
- 50% (EC50) = **69.3** %

**Figure 5**

Figure 5 shows an extract from the Report, it can be seen that with a 20% concentration of the wastewater, the respiration rate at 120.2 mg $O_2$/l/hr is 3-4% below the respiration rate of the control sludge. With increasing concentration, the percentage inhibition progressively increases. The plot of the relationship is shown in Figure 6.

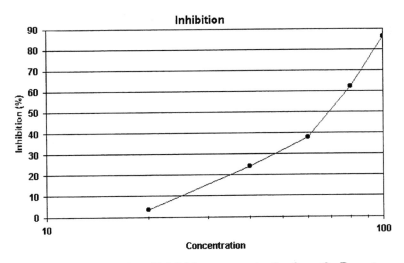

**Figure 6 The plot of inhibition v concentration from the Report.**

The software has calculated the concentration causing 5% inhibition ($EC_5$) to be 21.1% whilst the $EC_{10}$ is 24.9% and the $EC_{20}$ is 34.8%. These values clearly show that the waste is toxic. The plant manager then has to decide what level of inhibition is acceptable in the treatment tanks. In the study carried out at the Antwerp sewage treatment works, an average 10% inhibition did not appear to affect the quality of the effluent. Probably most managers will opt for a more cautious approach and accept a 2-5% inhibition. Unfortunately there is still a dearth of information on the effects of low levels of toxicity on the treatment process. It may be that process control models such as the Activated Sludge Model 1 (7) referred to above will, in time, be adapted to assist in decisions of this sort.

The final stage involves the calculation of the dilution of the waste which would be achieved when discharged into the system, from knowledge of tank volumes and flows. From this it is then possible to calculate the rate of discharge required to achieve the acceptable level of inhibition.

## SUMMARY

The management of toxicity at sewage treatment works is becoming of increasing importance in view of the increasingly more stringent environmental legislation which is being enacted. Whilst the legislation is targeted primarily to control of the quality of effluents discharged to receiving waters, there is a knock-back effect on the management of biological treatment plants.

Evidence is already accumulating of toxicity affecting the functioning of treatment works which accept significant quantities of industrial wastewater. It seems likely that in the years ahead, toxicity management strategies, perhaps integrated into process control software programs will become increasingly common. These will rely upon more sophisticated on-line monitors to protect treatment plants, and upon data obtained by the new generation of laboratory respirometers which measure toxicity from the respiration inhibition of the receiving activated sludge.

From information which is now available, it seems likely that toxicity effects will increase the operating costs of biological treatment. Paradoxically, except for a small number of documented cases of catastrophic toxic shock, there appears to be virtually no information on these costs, in the public domain. Information of this sort is urgently needed in order for treatment plant managers to make informed decisions on how best to manage toxicity emanating from industrial wastes.

## REFERENCES

1. N Paxeus, *Organic pollutants in the effluents of large wastewater treatment plants in Sweden.* Water Research 30, 1115-1122. 1996

2. M Rebhun, N Galil, *Inhibition by hazardous compounds in an integrated oil refinery.* J. Wat. Poll. Contr. Fed. 60, 1953-1959. 1988

3. HD Monteith, WJ Parker, JP Bell, H Melcer, *Modeling the fate of pesticides in municipal wastewater treatment.* Wat. Env. Res. 67, 964-970. 1995

4. P Berthoux, R Fan, *Evaluation of treatment plant performance: causes, frequency and duration of upsets.* J. Wat. Poll. Contr. Fed. 58: 368-375. 1986

5. *Introduction to the National Pretreatment Program.* Office of Wastewater Management (4203), EPA-833-B-98-002. United States Environmental Protection Agency 1999

6. K Jönssson, C Grunditz, G Dalhammar, JLC Jansen, *Occurrence of nitrification inhibition in Swedish municipal wastewaters.* Wat. Res. 34, 2455-2462. 2000

7. AD Andreadakis, CM Kalergis, N Kartsonas, D Anagnostopoulos, *Determination of the impact of toxic inflows on the performance of activated sludge by wastewater characterization.* Wat. Sci. Tech. 36, 45-52. 1997

8. E Hayes, J Upton, R Batts, S Picken, *On-line nitrification inhibition monitoring using immobilised bacteria.* Wat. Sci. Tech. 37, 193-196. 1998

9. P Grau, DP Da-Rin, *Management of toxicity effects in a large wastewater treatment plant.* Wat. Sci. Tech. 36,1-8. 1997.

10. D Geenens, C Thoeye, *The use of an on-line respirometer for the screening of toxicity in the Antwerp wwtp catchment area.* Wat. Sci. Tech. 37, 213-218..1998

11. M Henze, CPL Grady Jr, W Gujer, GvR Marais, T Matsuo, *Activated sludge model No 1.* IAWQ Scientific and Technical Report No I, IAWQ London. 1986

12. COST 624. European Concerted Action 624 *Optimal management of wastewater systems.*

13. JB Copp, *Defining a simulation benchmark for control strategies.* Water 21, 44-49. 2000

14. MN Pons,H Spanjers, U Jeppsson, *Towards a benchmark for evaluating control strategies in wastewater treatment plants by simulations.* Escape 9, European symposium on computer aided process engineering. Budapest 1999

15. J Benedicto, H Spanjers, *Personal communication.* 2000

16. H Spanjers, *Personal communication.* 2000

17. NG Love, CB Bott, *A review and needs survey of upset early warning devices.* Final Report Project 99-WWF-2, Water Environment Research Foundation. 2000

# Delivering savings in sludge tankering: opportunities and barriers for future development

*Geoffrey Sampson*
*BHRSolutions*

## ABSTRACT

Following the AMP 3 determination, there is increasing pressure on all areas of the water utility to improve efficiency and cut operational costs. As applied to the sludge strategy and associated transport business, this means improving utilisation of resources available (i.e. treatment and disposal facilities, vehicles and labour).

This paper describes the issues surrounding the potential for making savings associated with sludge tankering in the UK. Initiatives to improve efficiency are described, emphasis being on the potential benefits to be gained from inter-site logistics planning using software-based decision support tools. A case-study is used to quantify the significant savings that can be made under current operating regimes. The paper ends with a summary of more general opportunities and describes the barriers to be overcome and changes necessary before benefits will become more widespread.

## 1   INTRODUCTION

The requirements of the Urban Wastewater Treatment Directive and the introduction of the safe sludge matrix have focussed attention on sewerage service providers' ability to treat biosolids to higher levels, and secure acceptable outlets for the material produced. Investment in new treatment plant (and processes) has been essential and the costs associated with sludge have been seen to rise rapidly, and are forecast to continue to do so for the foreseeable future. As such, sustainable biosolids management (in cost and environmental terms) has become a priority throughout the industry.

With new works coming online and an increase in fuel prices, the costs of sludge tankering have increased. In the wake of the need to drive down costs this has inevitably brought the spotlight on this component of the biosolids supply chain. An industry-wide perception has developed that tankering represents a major opportunity for efficiency improvements to be made. Only now are commercial pressures prompting sludge tanker operators to review their working practices and to look at initiatives and technology embraced by third party logistics (3PL) operators over the last 15-20 years.

## 1.1 Sludge tanker management in the UK – past practice

The operation of sewage treatment works (STWs) in the UK results in significant quantities of liquid sludge requiring downstream treatment, typically at large works referred to as sludge treatment centres (STCs). The distribution of sludge between these points and on to final disposal is governed by the sludge strategy in place within each water company. The costs of running such systems vary as a function of the number, capacity and process characteristics of the STWs, STCs and recycling outlets available. This is in conjunction with the quantity of sludge requiring treatment, and the condition, performance and hence serviceability of the assets in place to handle it.

The means by which sludge distribution is managed within these systems depends upon a number of factors, primary of which can be considered as:

- The contractual arrangements in place within each service provider (i.e. whether the tanker operation is retained in-house or sub-contracted).

- The working practices adopted (i.e. whether the tanker operator is reactive to the de-sludging requirements of STWs and STCs, or bases operations on a forward-looking demand plan).

- The location and physical characteristics of the assets in place (i.e the storage capacity and de-watering techniques employed, and the size and carrying capacity of the tanker fleet).

- The historic practices and staff expertise retained within the relevant organisation(s).

In the majority of cases, inter-site sludge tankering operators are reactive to the needs of the asset operator, providing what is in effect a taxi service for STWs and STCs as and when de-sludging is required. A common arrangement is for works to request that a quantity of sludge or number of tanker loads be collected, typically on a weekly basis. It is then the fleet operators responsibility to collate the calls for the coming week and assign vehicles and drivers to that work. The majority of this work is carried out manually, from the scheduling of drivers and vehicles, to the release of jobs lists, all of which is labour intensive. Current system performance is thus largely dependent upon the experience and capabilities of the staff involved in running each regional operation.

## 2    THE CHANGING PICTURE

In a bid to reduce operational costs and redundant capital, most operators have shed vehicles that are superfluous to requirements. Rationalisation of operating regions has occurred in a number of companies with divisional control being replaced by centralised deployment. The adoption of alternative shift-patterns has also received attention, with emphasis being on the possible introduction of double-shifting, resulting in movements around the clock (works access and environmental constraints permitting).

Increasing competition in the water industry, along with indications that the splitting of asset ownership from operation may increase, has led commercially run tanker firms to realise that demonstrable efficiencies in operation will lead to new business opportunities around the UK.

## 2.1    Planning and monitoring initiatives

In terms of trip planning, the focus of attention for system operators has been on how best to order and schedule tanker movements, the objective being to minimise 'dead mileage' and to maximise value from the available assets.

There is a perception within those companies that currently operate tankers on a reactive basis that an element of forward planning could, and should, be implemented; this being particularly true in the case of 'milk-round' collections (i.e. pick-ups from large STWs within the system that require de-sludging on a regular, weekly basis). The logic behind this is that any activity planned in advance has the potential to be more efficient than one carried out in a reactive manner. A consensus appears to be emerging that it should be possible to plan 70-75% of journeys in advance.

Forward planning is one of a number of initiatives being addressed by operators in their bid to meet the cost saving targets being set by the UK water utilities. Figure 1 provides a schematic representation of the technologies and software applications available to support these initiatives, and how they contribute to delivering increased efficiency.

The technology required to develop integrated management and control systems is available, albeit in bespoke components that may not have been tailored to biosolids applications. Such systems comprise those technologies presented in Figure 1, along with features such as the increased use of telemetry at works (i.e. weighbridges and sludge tank level indicators).

The barrier to widespread development and adoption of integrated control and management systems, as applied to sludge tankering, is cost. The leap from existing practices is too great for many operators, especially where the risk rests with the water company. Fleet managers tend to be caught up in day-to-day operational issues that prevent sufficient time and resources being given to strategic initiatives that may or may not deliver immediate paybacks.

There is a clear need for services that enable the water companies and their tanker fleet operators to identify immediate opportunities to make operational savings, via an approach where the risks are shared between the client and the service provider.

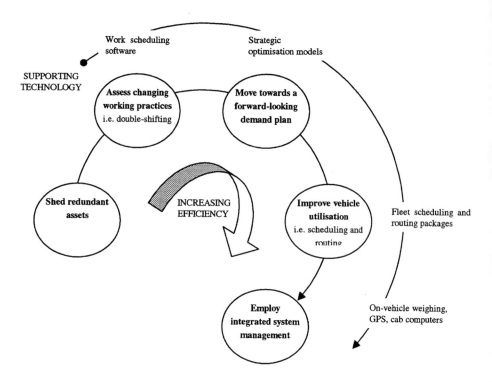

**Figure 1 – Initiatives available to fleet operators to deliver savings in sludge tankering**

## 3    IDENTIFYING SAVINGS THROUGH IMPROVED SCHEDULING AND ROUTING

BHR*Solutions* has carried out a number of sludge modelling studies encapsulating the logistics of sludge distribution within evolving management strategies.  The aim of these has been to introduce waste water and tanker fleet managers to the potential benefits to be derived from informed strategic and operational planning using software-based decision support tools.

The services offered are targeted at the optimum strategic distribution of sludge between points in the supply chain and associated long-term investment planning in the management network, as well as efficient fleet utilisation through improved vehicle scheduling and routing. The case-studies below demonstrate how the latter can be applied to sludge tankering systems in order to identify opportunities for cost savings.

### 3.1 West of Scotland Water case-study

A pilot study has been carried out demonstrating the application of BHR Group's tanker scheduling and routing service within the Ayrshire operational region in West of Scotland Water (WoSW). The aim of the work was to demonstrate the potential efficiencies to be made through more efficient tanker utilisation within a small region where operational data was readily available.

Five tankers currently operate in the region working out of a main depot at Underwood STC (Cumnock), and one ancillary base (Dalmellington STW), as shown in Figure 2. WoSW provided information on the sludge generation rates and storage available at each of the works, along with location, fleet profile and details of operational constraints, so that analysis of the optimum schedule could be made.

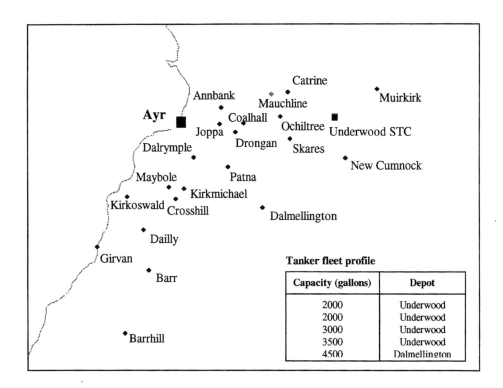

**Figure 2 – Site network and details of the fleet profile within the Ayrshire pilot study**

### 3.1.1 Method and work details

In setting up schedules for inter-site sludge tankering systems, a number of baseline parameters need to be set describing the operational constraints on the system being studied. This primarily requires information on the fleet profile, the labour resource available, and the interaction of these with each of the works in the system. This section summarises the tasks carried out which led to production of initial schedules for the Ayrshire pilot.

#### 3.1.1.1 Baseline data set-up

System constraints were set up in the scheduling software based on the following parameters:

- Definition of the customer base. Works location (grid references or post codes), opening hours and vehicle access restrictions.

- Construction of the fleet profile. Number of vehicles, their carrying capacity and depot origin.

- Determination of operational constraints. Driver duty, turn-around time (time to load and unload) and assumed road speeds on each carriageway type.

#### 3.1.1.2 De-sludging requirements

For each sludge-producing works within the system, analysis of the theoretical number of loads to be taken off site, on a weekly, monthly and annual basis, was carried out. Where available, actual 'sludge make' figures were used. In all other cases, theoretical arising figures were applied.

The number of loads collected from each works was based on the premise that the maximum vehicle size possible is utilised at all times. Maximising use of the largest tankers (i.e. the cheapest assets) is a priority in identifying potential cost savings.

The loads data-set was separated on the basis of works that form part of the core schedule (i.e. those requiring 1 or more collections per week), and those requiring regular monthly pick-ups. Owing to the nature of the schedule generated (i.e. one that is based on a weekly jobs list), works requiring a small number of collections over the period of a year were excluded from the modelling process. These can be easily scheduled, as and when collections are required, utilising identified slack in the core schedule.

A profile of core calls requirements was produced over a number of weeks in order to identify how the loads requirement potentially changes on a weekly basis. For example, the theoretical 'sludge make' at any given site might mean that in week 1, two tanker visits are required, but the following week, only one is necessary. The aim of this was to identify the worst-case scenario in terms of de-sludging requirements. Assuming the heaviest workload can be scheduled, it stands to reason that the baseline requirements can easily be catered for given the resources available.

The outputs derived from the processes described above, formed the basis of the calls data fed into the model for each schedule produced.

### 3.1.1.3 Schedules generated

The scenarios for which schedules have been produced are as follows:

a)     Core schedule containing week 1 pick-ups for those works requiring regular de-sludging

b)     Core schedule containing week 2 pick-ups for those works requiring regular de-sludging

c)     Schedule containing week 1 core schedule pick-ups plus weekly requirements of those sites requiring 1-3 collections per month

d)     Schedule based on existing calls frequency

### 3.1.2 Findings

The modelling runs for the core schedules (a and b above) identified that the de-sludging requirements from those works producing the majority of the sludge in the region (i.e. those requiring more than 1 call per week) could be carried out using solely the largest, 4500 gallon tanker. Utilisation of this vehicle is understandably high, near to 100% over the course of the week.

Adding in the likely calls from those sites requiring up to a few collections per month (scenario c above), the schedule produced utilises the 4500 gallon tanker near full-time, with only part-time contributions from the 3000 and 3500 gallon tankers. A similar situation occurred in the schedule based on the existing calls frequency (scenario d).

The results of the study would suggest that the tankering service in the Ayrshire region could be carried out using just three of the existing five tankers. The assumption is that all septic tank emptying requirements and calls to small works could be covered by one of the 2000 gallon tankers (as is currently the case). Emergency cover and periods of vehicle maintenance could be assigned to either the 3000 or 3500 gallon tanker, both of which are under-utilised within the schedules produced. The two spare tankers could be re-assigned to other regions where they may be more productive, or used to reduce the need for hired-in help.

Previous experience has shown that it is not always possible to extrapolate regional improvements in savings to the whole undertaking, due to local differences, including the distribution of arisings and treatment works, topography, fleet make-up and current practice. However, a survey of the study region relative to the whole of WoSW suggests that extrapolation in this case is reasonable. Currently, sub-contractors account for over 37% of the company's tankering costs, and the majority of the savings can be realised by reducing the need for hired-in help.

Extrapolated across the whole of WoSW's fleet of 43 tankers operated in-house, savings of between £300,000 and £500,000 per annum could be made by making more efficient use of the vehicles and drivers available.

WoSW have been receptive to the changes and benefits, and discussions are under way to determine the best method of achieving the potential savings, in line with their corporate strategy.

## 4    SUMMARY OF OPPORTUNITIES AND BARRIERS

The case study has shown that there are very significant savings to be made in the short term, at low risk, and it would be tempting to believe that other companies similarly are reviewing their sludge tankering costs, in a bid to reduce operational expenditure. Unfortunately, it will be some time before there is a general move to make cost savings in tankering. This is due to the structure of the industry, a tacit acceptance that sludge is a baseline cost, a lack of directorial responsibility for savings, a failure to empower and reward staff to seek and make savings, and that greatest of all barriers, entrenched current practice.

### 4.1    Opportunities

Opportunities to improve the efficiency of sludge tankering operations fall within the following groupings:

- **Revised operating practices.**  Initiatives such as double-shifting, improved tanker ordering at works and removal of internal operating boundaries between regions.

- **Adoption of technology to improve monitoring and control.**  Vehicle-mounted GPS units facilitate tracking of tankers and performance monitoring.  When linked to in-cab computers and traffic management systems, real-time scheduling and routing of vehicles is a viable, albeit expensive, option.

- **Introduction of software to aid strategic planning and operation.**  Selective use of software provides fast and flexible decision support, reducing manual scheduling tasks that are labour-intensive and lack mental stimulation.  Facilitating analysis of a range of 'what-if?' scenarios (e.g. the impact of changing driver shift-patterns), software can be used for strategic planning, including identification of the optimum mix of vehicles and depot configurations when bidding for new work.  As experienced staff leave the industry, taking with them in-depth knowledge of the tanker systems being operated, such tools will be of increasing value when planning sludge logistics.

- **Increased competition.**  New business opportunities exist for those operators willing to adopt strategic and operational planning techniques and work ethics embraced within 3PL operators.  Marginal areas in the vicinity of boundaries between operating divisions (either within the same company, or inter company) represent clear areas where economics can be improved, either through increased revenue or operational savings.

## 4.2    Barriers

First-hand experience of carrying out tanker logistics studies has shown that the main barriers to achieving increased efficiency are as follows:

- **Workforce utilisation.** The ability of the industry to introduce new working practices and conditions limits the delivery of efficiencies based on more effective vehicle utilisation. Where operations are run in-house, based on practices and attitudes entrenched in the days of public sector control, improvements in performance may be hard to deliver. Workforce availability may also hinder efficiency drives; the industry predicts that by 2004 there will be a shortage in HGV drivers of 20,000 each year.

  Legislation in the form of the Working Time Directive (to be introduced in Spring 2004) will restrict the working week to 48 hours maximum. This will not affect most in-house fleet operators but may reduce an outsourcing trend, driving up logistics costs as drivers want no reduction in income for less hours. The average working week for drivers in the logistics industry is currently 55-60 hours.

- **Contractual arrangements.** The way in which contracts are set up may not encourage fleet operators to identify efficiency drives in partnership with the asset owner/operator. A common area of inefficiency is the movement of part-loads between points in the management chain. If operators are paid by the tanker load, with no policing of the quantities moved, they will be keen to maximise rather than minimise trips.

- **Plan attainment.** A stumbling block associated with running operations based on a forward-looking plan is that unexpected events can result in the plan being overtaken by the need to take short-term corrective actions. Years of operating on a reactive basis make it hard to introduce what can seem like radical changes to operating practice.

- **Communication within the supply chain.** If positive change is to happen, new policies and working practices need to be effectively communicated and fully adopted throughout the supply chain. Communication between works operatives, regional managers, fleet operators and asset owners must be improved. Past practices should be reviewed; just because two tankers have historically been requested at a works each week this does not mean that it is necessary to do so. Improved communications will minimise occurrences such as aborted trips.

- **Asset limitations.** Access restrictions, unreliable plant and poorly specified equipment all limit efficiency. As an example, where sludge has not been dewatered to the desired targets, money is spent tankering water around the countryside.

It is fair to say that none of the stated barriers are insurmountable, the tackling of each representing an opportunity to introduce positive change.

# 5 CONCLUSIONS

It is clear that opportunities exist to make significant savings associated with sludge tankering, these savings being realised through adoption of efficient working practices and use of available technology. The initiatives described within the paper go some way to helping water utilities carry out informed planning and future investment associated with sludge logistics, along with implementation of more efficient practices on a day-to-day basis.

It is undeniable that as the industry is re-structured with contractual relationships developing between owners and operators of assets, the pressure to make cost savings will increase. Under the new structure it is hoped that the changes will elevate the importance of sludge treatment and disposal, with the realisation that efficient operation and cost savings are not only desirable but also mutually achievable. Those companies prepared to capitalise on the opportunities available now, shall be in a strong position to expand and win new business in the future.

BHR*Solutions* has developed a sludge logistics modelling service with a proven capability to help operators identify and realise the potential savings that can be made, via a shared-risk approach. Working in partnership with clients, our aim is to help the industry move towards a position where truly sustainable biosolids management (in cost and environmental terms) is achieved.

# Tracking sludge movements – an integrated solution

*Peter Jackson [1], John Waters [2] and Jim Arnot [3]*

*(1) (2) Entec UK Ltd, (3) West of Scotland Water.*

*This paper was first presented at the Aqua Enviro/CIWEM 5th European Biosolids and Organic Residuals Conference, Wakefield, November 2000. Published by kind permission.*

## 1.    ABSTRACT

There is an increasing need to provide effective tracking of sewage sludge to and from treatment centres to meet the requirements of the directive on sludge to land and the need for auditable records for all sludge movements. In the future it is likely that producers will be required to track not only sludge movements from treatment centres to final disposal, but also from the source.

Working closely with West of Scotland Water, Entec has developed a comprehensive **S**ludge **T**ransaction **A**nd **R**ecords system (STAR) to track sludge from the point of pick-up through processing to the final point of disposal. This system is designed to be fully integrateable with business IT systems including most common databases, GIS and laboratory systems.

The system hardware and software are completely modular, allowing the system to be configured for basic or highly comprehensive logging roles. Generally, the system comprises of three main features.

### 1.1    Vehicle Mounted Equipment

Records the weights and loads in the tankers or vehicles, and the related information e.g. customer ID, date and time of collection, or downloading, relevant GPS reference, operation of key vehicle systems, e.g. PTO, valves etc. All the information is stored on board in a removable flash memory card.

### 1.2    Site Logger

Takes the information from the flash card, checks that the load has come from a site authorised to be discharged at that point and then controls the download operation. Upon completion, all the information is then forwarded on to a central database system. The site logger can handle a selection of import lines from tankers, pipelines and weighbridges and a similar arrangement of export lines. Gate control systems, carrier verification, swipe cards etc., can all be provided as part of the system if necessary.

## 1.3    Central Software

Comprises of two main modules, the first is a transaction reconciliation module, which collates all the information from all the loggers connected to the system and forwards automatically reconciled information onto the database and holds a separate exception list of non-reconciled files for manual processing.  The second part is the main database system e.g. Gemini, which stores all the relevant information and links with other IT packages.

This paper will describe the main business drivers and reasons for providing sludge tracking systems and the technical details of the vehicle system, site logger and central database.

## 2.    INTRODUCTION

Typically, records of sludge movements by users in the past, have generally been quantified by the number of tanker or skip loads delivered to a given point of treatment or disposal.  In turn the number of loads were then converted into tonnage or volumetric measures, based on estimates of the amounts carried by each tanker or skip.   Generally records were then manually updated and totally dependant upon all loads been properly recorded whether carried by in-house vehicle fleets or external contractors.  Many of the pick up and delivery points were un-manned and consequently verification and authentication of loads was often impracticable.   On occasion more accurate information supplemented the estimates with weighbridge and flow meter measurements.

The scope for inaccuracies and inconsistencies within such records is considerable despite the best efforts of operators.

Today however, ever changing and more demanding business drivers require improved and accurate reporting systems suitable for external audit purposes.  Technology advances can now offer systems that can partially or fully automate all data collection and recording functions and provide the necessary auditable records at reasonable cost.

This paper is intended to raise awareness of the current available technologies illustrated by a specific application developed by Entec jointly with West of Scotland Water.

## 3.    BUSINESS DRIVERS

The main business drivers are generally well understood by users however, a number of them are assuming increasing levels of importance. Understandably, there will be differences in the priorities between operators and sludge producers depending upon local pressures and immediate needs. The following discussion summarises the main business drivers common to most operators within the water industry in the UK at present. Not surprisingly, the trend is to provide more accurate detail at each stage of the sludge transaction process to meet the needs of one or more of the business drivers.

## 3.1 Legislative

The main statutory instrument that applies to this area is EEC Council Directive 86/278 1986 on the protection of the environment, and in particular of the soil, when sewage sludge is used in agriculture. The requirements of this EEC directive form the basis of the 1989 Sludge (use in agriculture) regulations 1989. Further clarification of the regulations was given in the code of practice for agricultural use of sewage sludge issued by the DOE in 1996.

These regulations establish a need on all sludge producers to maintain records giving the following details:

a)     The total quantity of sludge produced in any year

b)     In relation to the sludge supplied for the purpose of use in agriculture, in any year -

    (i.)     The total quantity of sludge produced in any year;

    (ii.)    The composition and properties of that sludge as determined in accordance with Schedule 1;

    (iii.)   The quantities of treated sludge supplied and the type of treatment;

    (iv.)   The names and addresses of the persons to whom the sludge was supplied; and

    (v.)    The address and area of each agricultural unit on which sludge has been used, the quantity of sludge used thereon, and the amount of each of the elements listed in the sludge table which have been added thereto;

c)     A copy of every analysis or assessment made under schedule 2, or in accordance with advice given for the purposes of regulation 8 (4), relating to the soil of an agricultural unit on which sludge has been used; and

d)     A copy of any advice issued for the purposes of regulations 8[(3)(a)].

Or in other words there is a statutory obligation for sludge producers to track and maintain historical records of sludge movements from the source, which in most cases will be treatment works or sludge centres, to final agricultural disposal.

However the existing regulations are currently under review by an EEC wide expert group on sludge. Although it is unlikely that the regulations will be updated within the next 2 -3 years it is worth noting current proposals include the following -

e)     Producers shall implement the quality assurance system for the whole process, i.e. control of pollutants at source, sludge treatment, the way that the work is planned and the land evaluated, sludge delivery, sludge application and the communication of the information to the receiver of the sludge. The quality assurance system shall be independently audited by auditors duly authorised by the competent authority.

f)     Producers are to be responsible for the quality of sludge supplied (even when the contractor takes care of sludge marketing and spreading) that should guarantee the suitability of sludge for use. Producers are to analyse the sludge for the agronomic parameters, heavy metals, organic compounds and micro organisms.

It is likely therefore that the new regulations when they do appear will incorporate the above requirements thereby increasing the need for detailed records suitable for audit purposes.

Currently the proposal still only makes specific references to the need to track sludge from the sludge treatment centres to the point of final agricultural disposal. However it could be inferred from the need to keep auditable records that there may be a need to keep more accurate records about the upstream origins of the sludge rather than at or after the relevant treatment centre. This would probably be dependant upon the origin of the sludge prior to the treatment centres, which for example could include industrial units or abattoirs, etc., It may even be the case that the regulations may yet evolve to include such a requirement before final publication.

In addition, all sludge produced by Sewage Treatment works whether treated or un-treated is also covered by the controlled waste regulations 1992 and the waste management regulations 1997. Again these require records to be maintained regarding sludge movements in addition to the obligations of the other regulations summarised earlier in this section.

## 3.2    Lost Revenue

The sludge movements operated within most Water PLC's within England or the Water Authorities in Scotland involve the use of external contractors or agencies. Contractors may be working on behalf of the Authority or PLC and effectively supplementing the internal tanker fleet arrangements, or may be working as external contractors who are operating a sludge collection service which they need to dispose of through a sludge treatment centre or sewage works, paying for the privilege of doing so.

This provides the Authorities and PLC's with 3 distinct problem areas;

- Internal tanker fleet operations

- Contracted tanker fleet operations

- External contractors and agencies

In each of the above situations in the past, it has proved difficult to monitor and manage sludge volumes or weights discharged into or indeed uplifted from treatment works.

Studies on internal tanker fleets show significant discrepancies in the amount of tankered or dry sludge movements. Similarly the use of external contractors to support internal vehicle fleets further compounds the accuracy of such records. However one of the main areas of overall discrepancy is the involvement of external contractors operating a self employed sludge collection service who often discharge without authorisation, or records, thereby avoiding payment.

All of these problems can be addressed by the use of suitable site based logging systems and can be enhanced by vehicle-mounted systems thereby providing a detailed audit trail for external inspection.

## 3.3    Contracted Sludge Treatment Services

With the advent of PFI schemes taking on responsibilities for sludge treatment centres, particularly in Scotland, there are issues around recording and maintaining registers of sludge delivered into such schemes and sludge delivered to final points of discharge. Typically, there needs to be an agreed system of charging for such services normally based on volumes or weights of sludge passed to the PFI contractor for treatment. In addition, if the PFI contractor intends discharging to agricultural land then there is still an obligation on the authority or PLC as the sludge producer, to maintain the register of records etc.

Site based logging systems can be used as basis of charging systems with PFI contractors or alternatively as part of check systems to support charging systems based on other methods.

As before, any sludge going to land can also be tracked using the vehicle systems in conjunction with the site logging systems.

## 3.4 Improved Vehicle Utilisation

A large part of running any tanker or vehicle fleet is the logistics organisation required. Matching vehicle routes, loads, capacities and actual needs, to any given day or week, is at best an approximate science. Better information about vehicle utilisation will provide management with the means of maximising utilisation thereby reducing costs. Historical data can allow management to review previous work and plan better for the future, whereas live data can be used to dynamically change the ongoing plan.

The management information available from logging systems can provide a detailed insight into vehicle usage and can spot for example extended travel periods or extended standing periods, which could be indicative of problems within the plant or other operational difficulties.

Although such logging systems may be limited to internal vehicle fleets initially, they can be extended into the contracting market if combined with an appropriate commercial structure and used to produce improvements across the board.

## 3.5 Audit Trail In The Event Of Incidents

With the types of manual records available in the past, tracking an incident or pollution event in a watercourse has required a certain amount of detective work and assumption. Automatic logging systems tracking sludge from source through to point of final disposal through treatment, can be used as part of an incident trail. This would allow incidents to be traced to the point of source quicker and more accurately than with present systems.

The potential would be there for the Authority or PLC to be able demonstrate to the EA or SEPA that the operator was within their consents and had acted responsibly in maintaining the concentrations of allowable pollutants to land etc. and that the problem therefore, lies elsewhere and is not the responsibility of the sludge producer.

## 3.6 Improved Management Information

Overall an integrated system capable of monitoring sludge movements including management information about vehicle utilisation, actual loads delivered to and from treatment centres and final loads delivered to the point of agricultural disposal or otherwise, can be used to improve planning.

Sludge movement operations can have KPI's (Key Performance Indicators) set that can be subsequently monitored and adjusted with hard evidence. Overall operational costs can be better monitored and contracted services can be better evaluated to help set rates for future contracts.

The main benefit of an automatic system, which provides comprehensive data management information, is that it increases the control of the Authority or PLC involved. The future will require more comprehensive and detailed records to be kept at each stage of processes to ensure that the environment is protected. Systems do exist now that can meet most of the requirements anticipated in the next few years and beyond. Properly designed systems can be implemented in a modular fashion in distinct discreet stages thereby minimising costs and maximising value for money.

The next section will describe a modular based system as developed by Entec with West of Scotland Water to meet their particular needs.

## 4. THE SOLUTION

### 4.1 "STAR" System Overview

The opportunity arose to assist West of Scotland Water in defining and sourcing a sludge transaction management system for use throughout their region. There was not an integrated single system then available in the market place, capable of delivering the functionality that West of Scotland Water required. Entec were engaged because of their considerable knowledge of sludge management systems and specific experience in the provision of sludge logging systems.

The first stage of the project was to fully understand West of Scotland Water's requirements, which helped to define the project into three main areas. Detailed specifications were then produced for the 3 main areas or modules.

Although the specifications were originally written to facilitate quotations from interested manufacturers they were subsequently used as the agreed 'User Specifications' for the project.

In the case of West of Scotland Water, the main medium term business drivers were, to meet the requirements of the EEC Sludge to land directive and UK Waste Management Regulations. Whereas there was more pressing short term aim to provide accurate information about sludge transactions within their own tanker fleet prior to the privatisation of most of their main sludge treatment centres under PFI schemes throughout their region.

### 4.2 System Architecture

The system has been designed to be completely modular to allow all features to be used or inhibited to suit varying applications thereby satisfying the needs of West of Scotland Water and beyond. The modular approach allows the system to be upgraded in the future to take advantage of further developments or additional requirements. The 3 main modules are:

- Vehicle Mounted Equipment

- Site Logger

- Central Software Database

The overall aim was and is, to provide robust solutions based on currently existing technologies and to minimise the development aspect of the project. The only area of substantial development was in the overall integration of the various suppliers, equipment, technologies and the controlling software. The details of the 3 main modules are discussed in more detail in the following sections.

### 4.3 Vehicle Mounted Equipment

On board vehicle weighing using load cell technology is well proven and provides a solid basis for the collection of weight data on a vehicle. In providing an audit trail of vehicle movements and activities, it is necessary to record the date and time of any transactions together with the location of the vehicle at the time, along with the relevant transaction data e.g. weight.

The system works with Global Positioning System (GPS) satellite technology as a proven source of location tracking, 'stamping' each transaction with position data.

All signals including those that identify the beginning and/or end of a transaction provide inputs to the on-board data storage system. Signals can be provided electronically or from limit switches, proximity switches or sensors linked to the vehicle delivery systems to identify changes of state.

The fidelity of the data collected is of paramount importance and the design of any on-board data collection system should be automated with minimum input by the driver.

In the development of the on-board vehicle weighing system consideration was also given to the type of vehicle on which the system was to be fitted. Rigid vehicles can readily use a load cell system mounted between the tank or skip support frame and the chassis. However, articulated vehicles require hybrid solutions to suit the type of trailer / tank suspension system which may require pressure transducers etc, to provide the required weight information.

The initial development of the STAR system for West of Scotland Water was based on

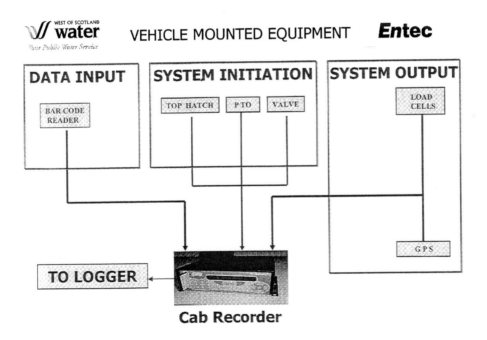

**Cab Recorder**

rigidtankers, which represents the majority of the vehicle fleet.

Input signals are taken from the discharge valve, top filling hatch and the power take-off (PTO), shaft to indicate vacuum pump on / off status.

Various methods of data collection, storage and transfer were considered amongst the technologies available, including storage of data to disk, storage to non volatile flash card and onward transfer via radio or satellite links to a central database.

The technology selected on the basis of simplicity, robustness and minimum capital outlay, was a non-volatile flash memory card system capable of storing several weeks of transaction data in its 1Mb capacity located in an in-cab card reader. Data stored in the flash card, is subsequently downloaded via a card reader direct to a PC data storage system or site logging system before onward transmission into the central database via a modem and PSTN line or corporate network system.

In order to minimise space requirements in the vehicle cab a combined card reader / weight indicator unit was developed for installation into the vehicle dashboard or overhead storage.

The card reader / weight indicator unit is the heart of the vehicle data collection and storage system developed for West of Scotland Water, however, a barcode reader is also provided for customer information, type of transaction and driver / vehicle ID, using codes printed directly on to operatives worksheets.

In operation a vehicle uplift or discharge transaction is initiated only when one of the following events occur.

a)  The customer ID bar code is scanned.

b)  The vehicle sensors detect a change of state.

Each transaction records the date, time, location, weight, driver and vehicle ID and status of each vehicle input sensor.

The on-board vehicle system can operate as a fully integrated system to record all the above data or selected data elements can be de-configured to suit, or additional sensors can be added.

## 4.4     Site logging facilities

Data collected via the vehicle on-board data collection system requires downloading initially into a site logging system or PC based card reader storage system. The system can be used in a stand-alone format or to forward data onto a central software database system to generate reports, trends and global information.

The simplest form of site logging system which would be used primarily to upload data from the flash cards used to store the transactions, comprises a card reader connected directly to a PC based data logger with communications capability. This arrangement would be used where the associated vehicle is not required to uplift or discharge sludge at that point, e.g. a depot.

Where there are a number of vehicle load discharge or uplift points on a site, networked operator interface panels would be provided at each point to provide drivers with an interface to the system to initiate discharges or uplifts and to transfer the data from the flash card.

Each operator interface panel requires a minimum of a card reader and screen display to initiate the data and load transfer and allow the driver / operator to view each stage of the process.

The operator interface panels provided to West of Scotland Water contain a card reader, HMI with touch screen display and menu selection buttons. Each panel is connected via a network to a site based PC data logger which can not only receive and store data of vehicle transactions but can also be configured to input data from weighbridges, site flow meters, suspended solid meters and level controls. Outputs to actuated valves, security barriers and CCTV monitoring systems, VCR's, etc., can also be provided if required.

Specially developed software in the site logger provides validation of contractors and their loads by comparing ID's and the load origins using GPS, against a list of approved sites stored in the logger thus ensuring that discharges to the site are only allowed from known and approved sources. This is essential in order to control access and provide auditable records of sludge / effluent sources and their point of discharge. The audit trail can be subsequently extended for transactions from treatment centres to land disposal sites.

The site logging system can interface directly with SCADA and site wide control systems and plant, or can be provided as a complete self-contained package including valves, pipe work, tanker terminals, flowmeters, etc.

## 4.5    Central Database Software

The Central Database Software system provides the focal point for the automatic transfer of data from each site logger system via PSTN or network links.

Data analysis modules within the software provide auditable functions and the detailed analysis of the data by:-

- Transaction source (including septic tank detail)

- Transaction destination

- Inter-site and Intra-site transfers

- Vehicle / Operator Identifier

The software can also export data for additional analysis into other commercial software packages e.g. Access, Excel, etc.

It also maintains the records of transaction data on-line for a user definable period whilst also providing reporting and analysis for both current and archived data.

For the West of Scotland Water development project the industry proven 'Gemini' central database system was selected. The system is designed to allow users to record all data relating to sludge production, sludge movement and sludge to land activity. A register of farmer's fields, with owner and contact details can be maintained within the core of the database system for access either directly or via a GIS package.

The central database system is linked to multiple site logger systems and the transaction data is automatically uplifted on a pre-determined basis from each site.

To enhance the flexibility of the central system, an additional software module was developed to automatically group and reconcile uplift and discharge transaction data across all site loggers, prior to entry into the central database system. Manual provision to edit un-reconciled data was included to allow the user to review unresolved transactions and system override occurrences. An unresolved transaction would be one where the load data from a tanker did not match the associated downloaded data via the site logger, for instance.

The central database software satisfies all legislative requirements for record keeping in the application of sludge to land for agricultural purposes as defined in Sludge (use in Agriculture) Regulations 1989 and the EU working Draft on Sludge 3$^{rd}$ Draft.

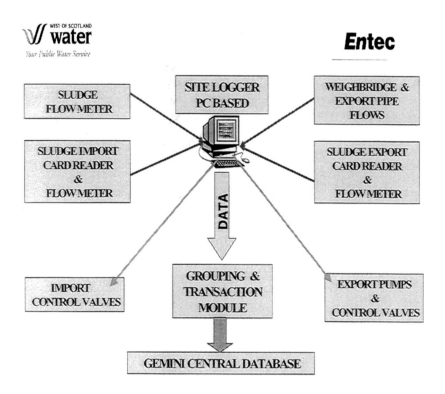

## 4.6 Summary

The overall system for West of Scotland Water was specifically designed for their in-house tanker fleet. The contractors currently employed to supplement the internal tankering service will interface with the system only at the site logging system level initially. They may be included within the vehicle-based systems at a later date.

## 4.7 Options

### 4.7.1 Barrier Control System

At unmanned sites a system of barrier controls with swipe card or auto detection systems, may be employed to gain access to, or egress from, the site. The site logger can provide the means of validating the authority of the contractor by storing a list of authorised contractors within the logger software. In such cases the logger may be located at the site or at a remote central database with modem or network communication link.

On validating the name of the contractor the logger can provide to necessary outputs to the barrier control system to allow the vehicle access to the site. Once on site, the contractor connects his tanker to the appropriate discharge point and enters details of the load, weight, type of sludge etc. into the site logger via an operator interface panel. Egress from the site is again via the swipe card reader or auto detection system, which provides the signal to the barrier control system to open.

### 4.7.2    Weighbridge Systems

At sites where the actual load discharged is used for billing purposes, it is more common to use a weighbridge as the means of determining the load by weight.

Weight data, time and date and contractor information can all be stored in the site logger via a data link.

The weighbridge module is an 'add-on' software module to the site logger system and integrates with the logger to pass the relevant transaction data on to the logger and subsequently on to the central software database.

### 4.7.3    Alternative Data Transfer Methods

Options other than the flash memory card are available to transfer data from vehicles to the site logging system using radio based systems with manually initiated or fully automatic transfers

### 4.7.4    Security Systems

The site logging systems can interface directly with CCTV systems and voice communications to facilitate remote site access by third parties. Visual records of each entry can be stored on local VCR's and tagged with the third parties details.

### 4.7.5    Option Integration

All options can be provided separately or as part of an integrated system.

## 5.    OPERATORS VIEW

One of West Of Scotland Water's main drivers for the provision of a logging system was that their experience showed that despite efforts to manage sludge operations and movements, there were still significant discrepancies in the system.  Check analyses and reviews of sludge movements, revealed significant errors between the tankerage volumes supposedly moved and the actual volumes recorded over several works.

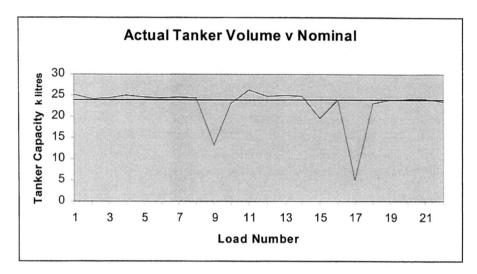

Management procedures alone were insufficient to fully rectify the situation.

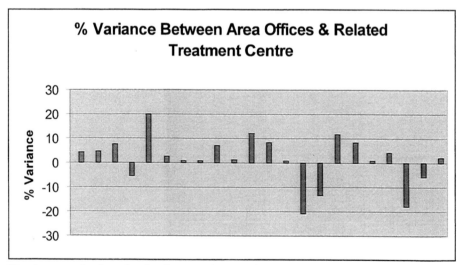

The above graphs show that the discrepancies were twofold.

The first graph shows that the operatives were wrongly assessing and recording the actual loads.

The variances in the second graph highlighted the inconsistencies between offices.

Initially West of Scotland Water Authority, decided to go to the market to see what the available technologies could offer to either automate or semi-automate or generally improve the overall situation. The conclusion unfortunately was that there were no readily available systems covering the operational activities from the point of original pick up of sludge through treatment to final disposal. Although a number of individual suppliers of sections within a potential system were identified, non of them were prepared to take on the overall role of providing a completely integrated system on behalf of West of Scotland Water.

As part of the exercise consultants were also considered as a means of taking the situation forward and Entec already had a logging system, which went part way down to meeting the objectives that West of Scotland had set for itself. The conclusion was that there was no viable alternative to meet the overall except to develop a system based as far as possible on existing technologies and existing products. Entec were appointed as the best people to take it forward. The overall cost of the system including the development and role out costs will be of the order of £900,000 spread over 3 years. This includes provision of vehicle-mounted systems to 30 vehicles, sludge logging systems based on 10 sites and a central database system.

The benefits will be, a better understanding of sludge movements and associated operations in greater detail than previously available. In addition the improved information will be used to drive out costs within the tankering operations and enhance the management of the interfaces with the PFI contractors and the final disposal points for sludge whether it be to land or otherwise.

A major benefit will be the production of properly managed and auditable records.

Medium term aims are to ensure that the system operates efficiently and effectively across the internal vehicle fleet in the first instance. Currently the contractors used in support of the in-house vehicle fleet only interface with the system at the site logging level initially but may be included in the vehicle mounted logging equipment at a later date.

## REFERENCES

- Statutory Instrument 1263 The Sludge (Use in Agriculture) Regulations
- 86/278/ECC Directive on the protection of the Environment, and in particular the soil, when sewage is used in Agriculture.
- Code of Practice for Agriculture Use of Sludge (DoE 1996)
- DETR Working Document on Sludge - 3rd Draft
- Statutory Instrument 1997 No. 351 The Waste Management (Miscellaneous Provisions) Regulations 1997.

# Impact of sludge thickening on sludge handling and management plan

*L Mountford MCIWEM [1], K Moran B.Sc, C.Eng, MICE, MCIWEM [2]*

[1] *Product Manager, Simon-Hartley,*
  *Stoke-on-Trent Staffordshire ST4 7BH. Email: lee.mountford@simonhartley.co.uk*
[2] *Treatment Manager, North of Scotland Water Authority*
  *Bullion House, Dundee DD2 5BB. Email: kevin.moran@noswa.co.uk*

## 1    ABSTRACT

The effect of regulations and policies upon sewage sludge treatment and disposal options have been well documented.   The more visible, large inner city treatment works have been identified for many years, and for the vast majority effective sludge treatment facilities now exist or are well into the design and construction phase.   However, there are also many smaller capacity works that will require enhanced sludge treatment, many for the first time.

Due to improved treatment standards, higher quantities of biological sludge is being produced for subsequent treatment, disposal or recycling.

Selection of sludge thickening equipment for these smaller sites shall be discussed. We will also detail End User considerations when incorporating thickening units at strategically situated locations within a region, the impact on tanker fleet size, tanker movements, operating costs and operator manning levels.

## 2    KEY WORDS

DAB System, Sludge Strategy, Whole Life Costs, Polymer, Power, Thickener Sludge, Tankers

## 3    INTRODUCTION

The introduction of mechanical sludge thickening at small sewage treatment works should be assessed on parameters, which when combined comprise a Sludge Strategy.   When considering this holistic view of sludge thickening and dewatering strategies, it is true to say that not all plants should install additional mechanical thickening equipment.   The return on the capital investment for plant should enhance the whole strategy and with minimal implementation risk.

In its most basic form, the objective when applying sludge thickening technology is to reduce sludge volumes. This reduction in volume can affect transport costs, treatment efficiencies at Sludge Treatment Centres and streamline operational costs.

The Paper will reference the Kirriemuir and Blairgowrie WWTP's from the Tayside Region of North of Scotland Water Authority (NOSWA). The contract for thickening equipment at the two sites was awarded to Simon-Hartley in November 1999, under the MF/1 General Conditions of Contract.

The objective of the project for NOSWA was to reduce the quantity of sludge transported from the two WWTP's by up to 80%. This would realise annual revenue savings by removing a road tanker from the fleet and improve environmental impact by reduced vehicle miles in accordance with the Authority's Environmental Policy.

Both these treatment plants had inadequate sludge storage and dewatering facilities on site, which could compromise plant operation and therefore incur high tankering costs.

The Capital Expenditure approval request had recommended a payback period of less than two years.


4    PROCESS SELECTION

The selection of thickening process equipment should compliment the overall Sludge Strategy of the Water Authority or Company.

The selection of mechanical sludge thickening equipment should consider the following parameters:

- Capital costs
- Process Performance
- Plant Footprint
- Operational Manning Levels
- Operational Costs
- Generally - Whole Life Costs
- Building/Plant Protection
- Environmental Issues and Planning

Traditionally, thickening plants have relied upon gravity sedimentation for the majority of process applications. Despite it's apparent simplicity and ease of operation, the consolidation tank has been much more successful with slurries having a high degree of inorganic particulate matter than those comprised solely of organic residues. The unstable composition of many organic and biologically active sludges has made prediction and control of performance more difficult, often varying significantly from site to site for similar applications. Subsequently, recent years have seen this particular process route being replaced by technical advances involving chemical flocculation and mechanical filtration as the primary method of separation. No more so than with biological sludges, where the use of mechanical thickening systems has been driven by the requirement to enhance the efficiency of treatment processes such as digestion and dewatering.

The selection of equipment for sludge thickening and dewatering will depend upon a complexity of issues, not limited to capital and operating costs, performance, manning levels and overall footprint.

Selection of the right equipment should follow the standard route of laboratory testing, followed by full-scale site demonstration of the actual machine and its performance. For sludge's that do not yet exist, reference visits to equipment operating on similar sludges are essential. Testing and site trials can be both time consuming and expensive, so it is worthwhile identifying some preliminary selection criteria to avoid duplication of effort and resource.

**Table 1 - Comparison of thickening equipment for small plants**

|  | Gravity Belt | Rotary Drum | DAB | Centrifuge |
|---|---|---|---|---|
| **Thickened Sludge** | A | A | B | A |
| **Throughput** | A | B | C | A |
| **Polymer Usage** | B | B | A | C |
| **Power** | B | B | A | C |
| **Capital Costs** | B | B | A | C |
| **Maintenance** | B | B | A | C |
| **Footprint / m3** | A | B | C | A |
| **Small** | B | B | A | B |

Table 1 is designed to give a rapid pre-selection of available options that can be obtained for the same sludge using different types of equipment. The ratings, (A = good, B = average, C = below average) should be taken as a guide only, since the positions may alter with sludge type, throughput or desired performance criteria.

The UK Water Industry in recent years has installed dewatering equipment at Sludge Treatment Centres, generally at the larger treatment plants with available treatment capacity for filtrate liquor returns, or, installing additional bespoke filtrate liquor treatment processes.

With their higher dewatering capacity, these Sludge Centres ensure minimal risk to the long term stability of the sludge recycling or disposal routes.

However, the overall cost of this operation can be considerably reduced if efficiency gains can be realised. These gains can be thought of as improved sludge quality, in terms of dewaterability or a decrease in overall volume.

A reduction in sludge volumes (albeit for the same dry solids quantity) at a Sludge Centre, will ensure that the dewatering equipment can operate at its optimum performance level.

For a given dry mass loading rate to the dewatering press, the lower the volumetric throughput, the longer the residence time of those solids within the press rollers. Subsequently, those solids then spend longer under pressure, which in turn allows the roller action to have an even greater affect in producing the highest possible cake dry solids contents.

The initial benefit to the Operation is that of reduced tankering costs. The utilisation of thickening equipment at remote satellite treatment plants will have a major affect on tanker requirements. The reduction in sludge volumes both minimising the number of tanker movements and possibly even the number of tankers required.

The selection process, together with the final plant design, should consider and take care to avoid the over thickening of sludges. This can result in viscous thickened sludge which is difficult to transfer to and from tankers and can be costly to pump. This is an even greater factor where the existing fleet of tankers is old, or, may not be designed for thick sludge material. Modern tankers can be designed to accommodate thick sludge, but the capital and operational costs associated with this type of operation tend to be prohibitive.

## 5    PROCESS TECHNOLOGY

### 5.1    The DAB Sludge Thickening System

The DAB System was originally patented in Scandinavia during the 1980's as a cost effective way of providing efficient sludge disposal facilities for isolated communities. Since then it has been adopted and developed for a whole range of industrial and municipal applications, which have benefited considerably from its simplicity of design.

The DAB system combine the benefits of both the consolidation tank and filter belt thickeners by utilising a traditional settlement tank design with an integral filtration mechanism (DAB Drainer). Fig.1.

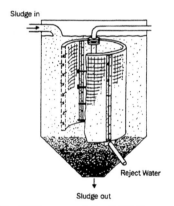

Fig. 1 Diagram of the DAB System

Incoming sludge is flocculated with polyelectrolyte and fed into the DAB silo where free water is allowed to drain away by gravity via the DAB Drainer, leaving the sludge solids to consolidate by gravity at the base of the tank. The DAB Drainer (Fig. 1), shaped as a double wall cylinder, consists of a framework of stainless steel or galvanised material covered by polyester filter media. When the Drainer is immersed in the sludge to be treated, the reject water (filtrate) flows through the filter walls into the hollow spaces between and drains by gravity away from the DAB.

156

Dependent upon the application, the DAB can be filled several times per day, compressing as it does the sludge present in the base of the silo. For thickening applications, the sludge solids can be drawn out on a regular basis by pump. If higher solids concentrations are required, further sludge can be added to the tank and then left to drain completely. This extra weight of sludge further compresses the sludge at the base of the silo significantly increasing the overall solids concentration.

The throughput of the system is maximised by having the filtrate valve fully open, and replenishing the system with new sludge as the level within the DAB begins to fall. Thickened sludge is then drawn from the base of the tank to meet the application requirements. The filter media is kept clean and functional by the use of an internal high pressure jet wash system (Fig. 2), using final effluent or recycled filtrate. The wash water is then retained within the silo until more sludge is added. Any solids associated with the wash water then bind onto the freshly flocculated sludge, the water being displaced with the rest of the filtrate via the DAB Drainer.

Standard DAB capacities of 2, 6, 10 and $25m^3$/hr are available, or specifically designed for the application. The DAB Drainer can also be used in isolation and retro-fitted to existing tanks or silos giving the option utilising current process design or a lower cost alternative.

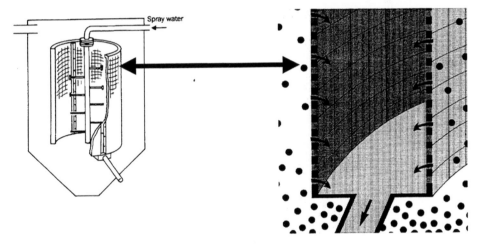

Spray water

**Fig. 2 Diagram of DAB Media Washing System**      **Fig. 3 Cross Section of DAB Drainer**

The DAB takes advantage of its built-in capacity to extend the overall filtration and consolidation time enhancing the final thickening performance (Table 2).

## Table 2  DAB Thickener Performance Chart

| SLUDGE TYPE | FEED SOLIDS (% D.S.) | THICKENED SLUDGE (% D.S.) |
|---|---|---|
| SAS | 0.5 to 1.5 | 4 to 7 |
| Oxidation Ditch | 0.3 to 0.7 | 4 to 7 |
| Co-settled | 1.5 to 3 | 6 to 8 |
| Primary | 2 to 4 | 6 to 8 |
| Digested | 1.5 to 3 | 6 to 8 |
| Water Works | 0.3 to 1.5 | 4 to 6 |

Filtrate produced by the DAB is of a very high standard (suspended solid levels as low as 10mg/l) and final treatment or polishing before disposal is often not required.

The DAB is ideally suited for small thickening applications, requiring no building coverage, minimal maintenance and occupying a very small foot print. Ancillary equipment, including sludge feed pumps and polyelectrolyte dosing, is required to complete the total installation.

## 6     OPERATIONAL CONSIDERATIONS

The current NOSWA Sludge Strategy, which has been further developed since November 1999, continues to utilise a philosophy of local thickening at rural or satellite WWTP's to 5% dry solids content prior to tankering to a Sludge Treatment Centre. At these Centres, the sludge is then dewatered via belt press, followed by lime addition to produce a stabilised cake at 40% dry solids for recycling to land as a beneficial fertiliser in accordance with the Prevention of Pollution from Agricultural Activity (PEPFAA) Code of Practice.

A summary of the Blairgowrie and Kirriemuir WWTP's prior to the installation of the DAB units can be found in Table 3 (below).

## Table 3 - Summary

| Parameter | Blairgowrie WWTP | Kirriemuir WWTP |
|---|---|---|
| Year Constructed | 1974 | 1985 |
| SEPA Discharge Consent | BOD 20mg/l<br>Ammonia 15mg/l | BOD 10mg/l<br>Ammonia 10mg/l |
| Population Equivalent | 8,000 | 6,000 |
| Inlet Screening | 3mm | 6mm |
| Primary Settlement | No | No |
| Treatment Process | Extended Aeration | Extended Aeration |
| Sludge Produced (approx.) | 250m$^3$/wk at 0.5 to 1.0% d.s. | 250m$^3$/wk at 1.5% d.s. |
| Sludge Storage/Dewatering | Inadequate | Inadequate |

From the extended aeration ditch wastewater passes into a final clarifier tank to allow solids to settle. Dilute sludge is drawn off from the base of this tank into an intermediate sludge buffer/holding tank. From that tank the sludge is fed into the DAB unit, where sludge is thickened to a final product of 5 to 6% dry solids. The thickened sludge is pumped into a further holding tank, awaiting collection by road tanker. The DAB unit filter is cleaned via the consistent high quality plant final effluent, which allows subsequent high drainage efficiency and performance. For the Kirriemuir and Blairgowrie sites, this equates to journeys of approximately 30 miles to its respective Sludge Centre.

The tankers are managed on a weekly programmed route by the Supervisor at the Sludge Treatment Centre. When these tankers discharge their sludge loads at the Sludge Centre, they log in via a swipe card system and are then monitored and logged via an IEA Data Logger. This data is then input into the IMASS - Gemini Sludge Management & Information System. This data is then available to the Supervisor for the subsequent planning of tanker Operations.

The DAB unit, together with the overall WWTP control, is linked via telemetry to the Regional Office at Dundee. From this point, plant status can be monitored and faults recognised as appropriate.

The immediate saving in tanker costs has been shown to realise a payback rate on the capital investment of much lower than the 2 years requirement that had been originally specified.

Following some initial commissioning problems with the polymer preparation system, the DAB System has operated to the satisfaction of NOSWA for 12 months. The plant realised its potential in terms of reducing tanker costs immediately.

In addition, these sites have required only 100 hours of combined plant operation and routine maintenance checks. A thorough electrical and mechanical inspection (taking 4 hours) of the DAB unit and its ancillary equipment takes place every 6 months.

The simple DAB System with its low number of moving parts has shown to give a very consistent maintenance requirement in the form of checks alone. Over the long term, this consistency of operational expenditure will allow improved planning and cost management.

**Fig. 4 Kirriemuir WWTP**     **Fig. 5 Kirriemuir WWTP**

An added advantage fo the DAB unit selection meant that there was no building required that would otherwise need to be maintained and heated.

# 7   CONCLUSION

The need for efficient and cost effective sludge treatment is now identified for all sewage treatment works, regardless of their size or complexity. The use of thickening and/or dewatering is a fundamental part of all current sludge treatment options. Selecting the correct equipment is subject to a variety of issues relating not only to actual process performance, but also to the real cost of installation and operation. Understanding these issues will help to minimise the long-term cost of ownership.

From Kirriemuir and Blairgowrie, together with other previously installed plant, NOSWA have now gleaned operational experience of the DAB units. This operation has been mainly trouble free from a maintenance perspective, whilst consistently achieving the required thickened sludge output dry solids to realise the tanker reduction.

To this end the original NOSWA project objectives have been achieved. The reduced environmental impact resulting from lower tanker movements have been shown by the operational cost savings associated with tankering. This has resulted in a payback on the capital investment of less than 2 years.

The success of these and other DAB projects means that NOSWA are looking to roll out still further their strategy of thickening at rural or satellite works and minimising tankering into Sludge Treatment Centres for dewatering by belt press.

# AUTHOR INDEX